The Wonderful World of
Prehistoric Animals

William Elgin Swinton

27 Paintings by Maurice Wilson

Garden City Books   Garden City   New York

Other books in this series

The Wonderful World
James Fisher

The Wonderful World of the Sea
James Fisher

The Wonderful World of the Air
James Fisher

The Wonderful World of Mathematics
Lancelot Hogben

The Wonderful World of Energy
Lancelot Hogben

The Wonderful World of Communications
Lancelot Hogben

The Wonderful World of Archaeology
Ronald Jessup

The Wonderful World of Medicine
Ritchie Calder

The Wonderful World of Food
John Boyd Orr

The Wonderful World of Life
Sir Julian Huxley

The Wonderful World of Transportation
Laurie Lee and David Lambert

The Wonderful World of Engineering
David Jackson

The Wonderful World of Prehistoric Animals

Editor	**Josephine Perry**	Artists	**Maurice Wilson**
Art Editor	**Edwin Taylor**		**Sidney W. Woods**
Assistant	**Malcolm Booker**		**G. Leigh Davies**
Research	**E. M. Robinson**		**Peter Sullivan**

© 1961, Rathbone Books Limited
Library of Congress Card Catalog No. 61-5589
Printed in Great Britain
by L.T.A. Robinson Ltd.,London

CONTENTS

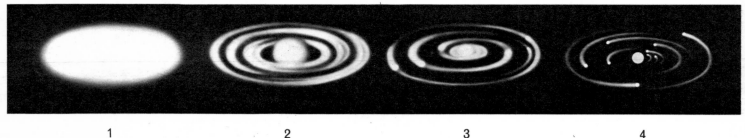

1   2   3   4

Our sun and its planets may have started as a whirling cloud of cosmic dust and gas (1, above). The central portion condensed to make the sun (2). Then the outer whirls began to pack together (3) until they became the nine planets (4). Opposite: the forming planets revolve round the sun.

Fossils: Clues to the Past

This is the story of the animals that lived on earth long ago. It is the story of the tremendous dinosaurs – of *Tyrannosaurus, Diplodocus* and their kin – but it is also the story of the small lizardlike animals that were the twenty-million-great grandfathers of the dinosaurs.

It is the story of the saber-tooth tigers, the giant sloths and the mammoths; of their ancestors, the small shrewlike animals which hid beneath bushes when the dinosaurs lumbered past.

It is the story of all the animals that lived in the sea, on land and in the air; from the smallest to the largest, from the first tiny one-celled creatures that lived 3000 million years ago, or more, to the woolly rhinoceroses and cave bears that Stone Age man hunted 30,000 years ago.

Our story is about prehistoric animals and the plants that provided them with food and shelter. Prehistoric means " before history," so a prehistoric animal is one that lived before men started to record in writing the events that happened and the things they saw and felt.

How, then, do we know what prehistoric animals were like? The answer is that some of these animals left clues to themselves in the rocks: clues we call fossils. We can learn a lot about the animals of long ago from these clues, and by comparing some of the fossils with animals alive today. But to understand how fossils are made, we must learn about the earth: how it was formed and how it changes.

Scientists who study the earth have worked out that our planet was born about 4600 million years ago. No one knows for certain how it was formed. One suggestion is that there was a great cloud of gas and dust turning round the sun. This cloud broke up into small whorls. These gradually packed tighter together as they turned and eventually became the planets that now move round the sun.

If this is how the earth was made, it may have been terribly hot from the start. Or it may have been cold to begin with, but made very hot later by the radioactivity of its own material.

The gases in the atmosphere round the young earth probably did not contain much water vapor. But as the earth began to cool down, the atmosphere changed. Gases like methane and ammonia must have been altered chemically and this produced more water vapor. Then the first rain fell. At first, this rain must have hit the still hot earth with a great sizzle and risen again as steam. But soon it came in torrents, cutting the first river beds and filling hollows to make the first lakes and seas.

As the rains fell, they washed bits of rock down into the sea. The seas ate into the cliffs, breaking great chunks of rock off them. Slowly this erosion wore down the land. Movements deep within the

More than 4000 million years ago, when the earth was young, the planet where we now live might have looked like our picture below. Under a lurid sky, bubbling rivers of molten rock may have flowed past the gaunt masses of rock that were the earth's first lands. All must have been hot: even the atmosphere that shrouded the young earth was still too hot to drop any rain.

In time, the earth began to cool down. As the steam in the clouds condensed, it fell to earth as rain. When these first raindrops hit the still warm earth, they probably sizzled up again as steam. But soon the rain fell heavily and the water began to run over the rocks in streams and rivers until it reached a hollow. The first sea on earth might perhaps have looked like this.

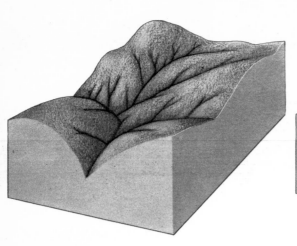

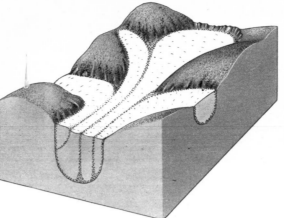

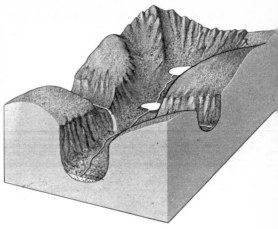

Streams and rivers, as they run through mountains, carry away pebbles, sand and mud; and leave valleys shaped like these.

If the climate is very cold, valleys may be filled by glaciers – slow-moving masses of ice – which wear away the valley sides.

When the climate gets warmer, the glacier melts, leaving valleys like these. Even the hardest rocks can be scraped away by ice.

earth caused hot lava to pour from rock cracks in volcanoes; or made earthquakes; or pushed up the earth's crust into new mountains. These changes, both wearing away and building up, have gone on since the earth was born, and still go on.

What happens to the pieces that are worn off the land? The rivers carry them down to lakes and seas, where they drift to the bottom. Slowly the layers of mud, sand and pebbles get thicker and thicker. If nothing happens to stir up this sediment, the layers at the bottom are pressed together by the weight of those on top, and eventually become rocks like sandstones, clays, limestones and so on. These types of rock are called sedimentary rocks because they are made from sediments.

But mud and sand and stones are not the only things a river carries away from the land. Have you ever seen a flooding river in full spate? In the thick brown water you can see leaves, twigs, logs, even

the bodies of dead animals, all being whirled away down to the sea. These, too, drift down to the bottom where the water is quiet. And they are joined on the sea floor by the dead bodies of animals that live in the sea.

As they lie on the muddy sea floor, the soft parts of dead animals are usually eaten by scavengers or decay away. But the hard parts, the shells, bones and teeth may remain. More mud and pebbles drift down and cover them and if this sediment becomes rock, the remains are entombed in it and become fossilized.

If sediments become rock at the bottom of the sea, then why do we find fossils on dry land? Because the sea bed in time may be raised by the great movements of the earth's crust. Many of our biggest mountains – the Rockies, the Alps and the Andes for instance – are made of rocks that were laid down at the bottom of ancient seas.

Mud, sand and pebbles drift to the bottom of the sea, where they form layers of sediment. The bodies of dead animals also sink to the bottom, and lie for a while on the top of the muddy layers.

Usually, the flesh of a dead animal decays away quickly, but the bones, teeth or shell may remain. Eventually, these hard parts are covered by more material, and are caught within the sediment.

Most, but not all, fossils are made in lakes or seas; sometimes animals may be caught and fossilized in muddy places on land, or drifted over with blown sand or dust which later becomes rock.

Fossil hunters are detectives who must let no detail escape them. When they find a fossil they are often quite puzzled about exactly *what* it is, and have to find more fossils, of the same and other kinds, before they can be sure. Like good detectives, they must be quite sure *where* they found their clue – not merely about the place, but about the kind of rock and the *precise level* in that rock. And – just as important as the rest – they must try to estimate when the fossil was alive.

Now the layers of sedimentary rock, which are called strata, form one on top of each other, so the oldest is at the bottom. Even though the strata may be tipped up or folded by earth movements, we can usually work out which was at the bottom originally. A fossil in a layer near the bottom of a series is older than one in a layer near the top.

Chalk is a white sedimentary rock made mostly from the shells of minute sea animals. Geologists have been able to calculate that it took about 30,000 years to make a depth of one foot of it. So if two fossils are 10 vertical feet apart in a chalk cliff, the higher is about 300,000 years younger than the lower.

This method of dating fossils is useful. It can tell us the relative ages of the fossils in a bed. But it cannot tell us the age of the bed itself unless we can collect together measurements of all the beds that have succeeded each other through geological time from the present back through the past. This is not so easy as it sounds, for most beds have been eroded, or folded by earth-crust movements, and are incomplete or changed in some way. Nevertheless we can arrive at a rough time-scale in this way (page 25) showing the depths of the rock-beds in each division of geological time.

Fossils formed fairly recently can be dated by the varve method, which is explained on this page.

The newest, most exciting and most accurate methods of dating rocks use radioactive materials in the rocks. The atoms in these materials gradually change into other atoms. For instance, an atom of uranium gives off a series of little parts of itself, until eventually it is changed into an atom of uranium-lead. Scientists know how long it takes for the half of any amount of uranium to become uranium-lead. It is about 4510 million years.

The slate and limestone in this cliff were laid down in flat layers, but the force of earth movements pushed them into great folds.

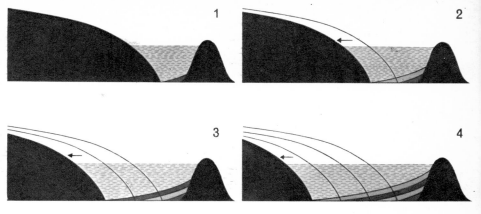

Rocks called varve clays can be dated in this way. As a glacier melts and retreats in the summer (arrows), pebbles, sand and mud are carried into the lake at its foot (dotted lines). The pebbles sink first, the lighter materials more slowly. These sediments form varve clays. The pebbles, sinking first, form a definite layer each year: so the number of such layers tells the age of the clay and of its fossils.

This chalk cliff in Dorset, England, is about 70 feet high; the numbers show 10-foot divisions. Scientists have worked out that it took 30,000 years for a layer one foot in depth to form; so each division represents 300,000 years. A fossil in division two would be over a million years older than one in division five of the cliff.

Certain rocks, when first formed, contained some uranium but little or no lead. Their present content of uranium and uranium-lead can be very precisely measured by new techniques. From the proportion of these, and from our knowledge of the " half-life " of uranium, a measurement of the age of the rock can be worked out with a small margin of error.

Scientists use several other radioactive materials besides uranium to date rocks in this way – but only rocks that were made from molten material flowing up from deep inside the earth. We call such rocks *igneous* – meaning fiery; and the trouble is that they are too fiery, when formed, to contain fossils. Sedimentary rocks may contain radioactive material; but we cannot use this to date them, for we have no means of telling when the radioactive rock in the sediments was worn off the original igneous rock it came from. So we have to rely on finding " sandwiches " to date the sediments. Fortunately these are not rare; layers of igneous rock between sedimentary rocks are fairly common, and when we date them we get a good clue to the age of the sediments above and below them.

The oldest rocks so far found are just over 3000 million years old; more than half as old as the earth itself. Of course, there must have been many even older rocks, but these are either lying deep beneath other rocks, or have all been worn away and re-made into sedimentary rocks.

Many sedimentary rocks that were formed a long time ago have been changed by movements of the crust of the earth. Rocks may be buckled and folded by great forces as two moving parts of the earth's crust press together, or the heat of molten rock flowing over or through them may partly cook them. Such altered rocks are called metamorphic rocks (from the Greek word *metamorphosis* which means change). Fossils are very rare in metamorphic rocks; most were destroyed or rendered unrecognizable by the metamorphosis.

Many fossils survive in sedimentary rocks that in turn become hidden, deep under later formations, where no fossil-hunter can penetrate to them.

So it is only by lucky chance that we can find clues in our detective story. First the animal must become a fossil; this happens only occasionally; usually an animal is completely destroyed soon after it dies. Next, the fossil must be preserved within the rock. Then its rock must escape metamorphosis: and then it must become accessible, or exposed.

Millions of years after a fossil was first formed in a layer of rock, it may lie deep under many other layers (far left). Earth movements, or an upward flow of molten rock (left, red arrow) may lift, fold and buckle the layers so that they are land instead of sea floor. Water, ice and wind wear away the new land until the fossil is exposed (below). The model, above, shows a landscape and underlying rocks. On the right is a mass of igneous rock, formed from a flow of molten rock. When this was pushed up, the layers of sedimentary rock (at left) were folded. Erosion has afterwards flattened the land. Mining tunnels pass through different layers to reach minerals that were deposited in cracks in the sedimentary rock.

Rocks, with fossils in them, are exposed by mining, tunneling, road cutting, but most usually by the forces of nature – by sea, wind, ice, rain or river wearing away the rocks around. And, of course, when the fossil is finally exposed it must be found by someone who knows that it is a fossil and that it has a story to tell.

Wherever men walked by cliffs, or along river banks, and wherever they dug deep into the earth, they must occasionally have found fossils. Over 2000 years ago a few Greek thinkers guessed that the fossils they found had something to do with animals. For instance, Xenophanes, who lived in the fifth century B.C., found fossils of fish, and other sea life, far inland, and he suggested that parts

In the past, men had strange ideas about fossils. Von Guericke made fossil bones into this unicorn in 1749. A fossil salamander (below), found in 1731, was called Homo diluvii testis: *it was thought to be the remains of a man drowned in the Flood.*

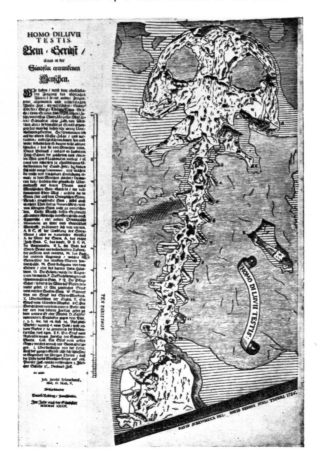

of the land were at one time hidden under the sea.

But these scientific writings about fossils were mostly forgotten and ignored during the Dark and Middle Ages. Some medieval people thought fossils were the work of the Devil when he tried to create animals. Others thought they were the bones of the fabulous creatures described by travelers.

Not until the Renaissance in the 16th century did anyone study fossils seriously again. Leonardo da Vinci recognized that fossils had once been living things, and that the position of land and sea had altered, land sinking under the sea, and sea bed rising to become land.

Despite this, most people continued to believe in the old theories. One favorite suggestion was that fossils were the remains of animals and men drowned in the Flood. But through the 17th and 18th centuries a number of natural historians were collecting, studying and writing about fossils. One of the greatest of these was Baron Cuvier, who lived from 1769 to 1832.

After the French Revolution, many houses in Paris were rebuilt with stone from nearby quarries. The rocks in these quarries contained many interesting fossils, particularly of backboned animals. Cuvier made a collection of these fossils and studied them. He was puzzled by the fact that each layer of rock had its own types of fossil animals. He suggested that every so often a tremendous catastrophe struck the earth, killing off all the animals. After each catastrophe, a new collection of animals was created. These, in turn, were killed by the next catastrophe.

In England at the same time, William Smith also noticed that fossils differed from layer to layer in the rocks. Smith was making canals, and as he traveled through England, he studied fossils. He was interested in them for what they could tell him about rocks, not only for themselves. He realized that some fossils could be used to mark a definite type of rock, for they were found only in that rock. Using fossils he mapped the types of rock all over England.

Smith's work was the beginning of the science of geology, the study of the earth. One of the fathers of this new science was Sir Charles Lyell (1797–1875). Lyell finally disproved Cuvier's ideas of great catastrophes. He also studied the ages of rocks, and made estimates of them, which are not too different from the ages we now think are true.

Lyell, and most other scientists of his day, thought that each different type of animal had been specially

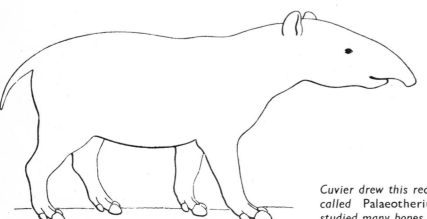

Cuvier drew this reconstruction of a fossil called Palaeotherium. *He found and studied many bones of this early mammal.*

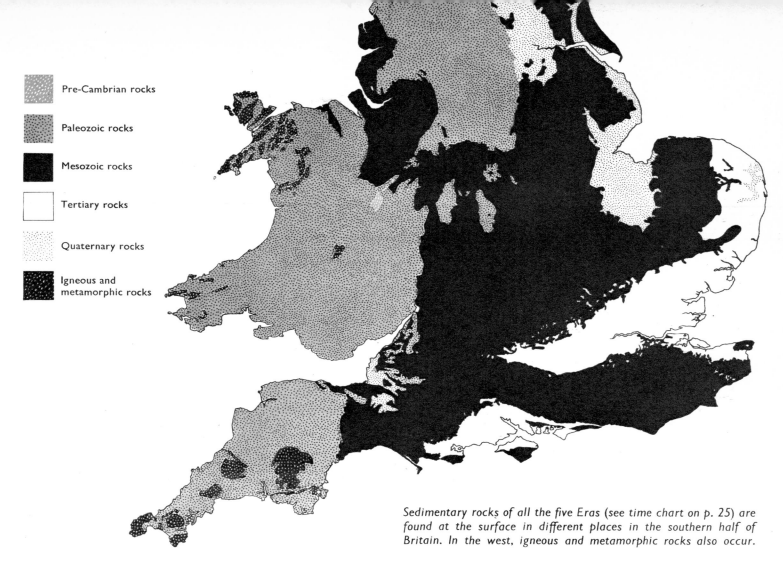

Pre-Cambrian rocks

Paleozoic rocks

Mesozoic rocks

Tertiary rocks

Quaternary rocks

Igneous and metamorphic rocks

Sedimentary rocks of all the five Eras (see time chart on p. 25) are found at the surface in different places in the southern half of Britain. In the west, igneous and metamorphic rocks also occur.

created by God. But by the middle of the 19th century a few scientists were no longer content with the "special creation" theory. Many problems worried them. For instance, why were so many animals, living and fossil, built on the same plan?

One of these questioning scientists was Charles Darwin. In 1831, Darwin sailed as naturalist on board a British surveying ship, H.M.S. *Beagle*, on a voyage round the world. When he was in South America, he found fossils of many animals which were like, but not the same as, the animals living in that continent now. For instance, he found fossils of an armored animal called *Glyptodon* (see page 67), that was like an armadillo. It occurred to Darwin that perhaps they were alike because they were actually related. Perhaps each type of animal was not fixed, but could change slowly into a new type.

This idea was not new. What was new was Darwin's ideas of how this change, or evolution, took place. He started from two facts: 1. that each species (the scientific name of an animal type) produces many more young than can possibly survive – think of the amount of frog spawn you can find in a small pond; and 2. that no two members of a species are exactly alike. And if animals vary, some must be better fitted to living their way of life than others. Darwin realized that these better-fitted animals had a better chance of breeding; and that their offspring would be likely to inherit the characteristics that gave their parents the advantages over the others. In this way a species gradually changes and improves. We call the process by which it does so, in its natural surroundings, natural selection.

Darwin's book, *The Origin of Species*, made people much more interested in fossils because it showed that fossils are the remains of the ancestors of the animals alive today. We can find series of fossils showing the changes that have made the animals we know. One of the best known series is that of the horse (see page 68).

What can we learn from rocks and fossils? Let us take a fossil and its piece of rock as an example. The fossil is a kind that we can find in a quarry near Liverpool, in England.

In this quarry, the rocks are a reddish color, which tells us that the rock was made from a desert sand. At some time in the past, then, this place near Liverpool was a hot, sandy desert. If we look

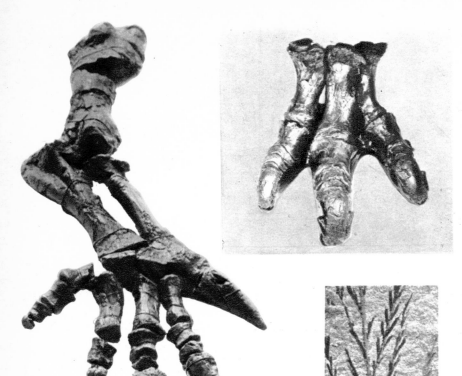

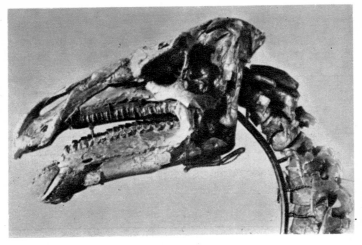

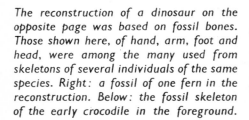

The reconstruction of a dinosaur on the opposite page was based on fossil bones. Those shown here, of hand, arm, foot and head, were among the many used from skeletons of several individuals of the same species. Right: a fossil of one fern in the reconstruction. Below: the fossil skeleton of the early crocodile in the foreground.

around, we might find a slab of this reddish rock that shows a change in the conditions long ago. On this slab we can see something which is very familiar. There are ripple marks on it, the same sort of marks we see on a wave-washed beach – but turned to stone. So the sand forming this slab of the rock was once part of a beach and, when the wind blew, the water rose up in waves and made these ripple marks.

Another slab of rock from this same quarry can show us something equally interesting. On the flat surface, where it has been broken out of the quarry, we may see the pitted marks of raindrops. If we can find several of these slabs and can work out their original position in the quarry, they will tell us the direction of the wind that blew the rain that made

these pitted marks nearly 200 million years ago!

Not very far away from our quarry, we may come upon the footprints of a number of little animals. Some of these footprints are rather like a human hand: there are five fingers and one is bent back like a thumb. But if we find a trail of these footprints we may be very puzzled for the " thumbs " are on the outside of the print (see page 22). When these little trails were first found scientists could not understand them. One even drew the animal walking with crossed legs so that its thumbs would be in the correct position! Later paleontologists realized that the fifth toe was not a thumb at all but a shorter outside toe that many reptiles have.

These footprints, then, were made by a little reptile. No one has found the bones of this reptile, but lots of footprints have been found and we have been able to work out much about the animal; where it lived and what it lived on, and therefore what it was looking for as it wandered about.

As well as these handlike footprints, we can find a number of much smaller footprints of little animals that apparently ran along in a lizardlike way. From other pieces of rock we can learn a little of the plants that grew in this sandy place.

In this way we can learn what it was like just outside Liverpool, 200 million years ago: the plants that grew there, the animals that lived there and what the weather was like.

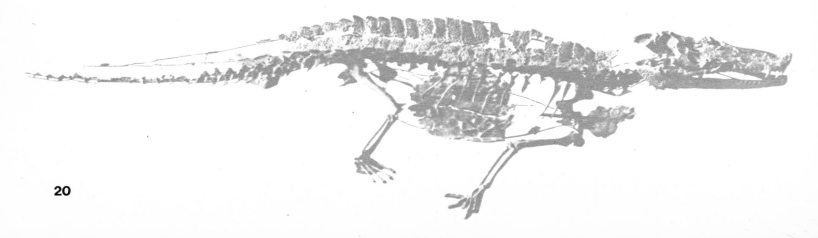

Iguanodon bernissartensis – as this dinosaur has been named – browsed in the Cretaceous forests of the land that now is Belgium. So well have its fossil remains been studied that the main guesswork in this reconstruction of Iguanodon concerns the animal's color.

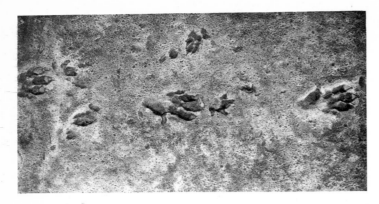

These handlike footprints are the fossil trail of a little reptile; the smallest toe is not a "thumb," but a smaller outside toe. Fossil footprints may tell us a great deal about the animal that made them.

The skin of a duck-billed dinosaur was pressed into the material that covered the dead animal 100 million years ago. When the sediment became rock, the imprint was preserved. Now we can trace the pattern of its hard skin, clearly shown in this unusual fossil.

So far we have written about what we can learn from rocks and fossils. Now let us see what fossils are.

Fossils are not usually the actual bone or shell as it was in the living animal. In the rock in which it is entombed, the material of the bone may gradually be replaced by other chemicals from the rock. It thus becomes rock, but keeps its shape.

Sometimes the remains of the animal decay after they are shut in the rock and the space where they were is filled with other material. Then we may get a cast of the outside of the animal.

In very special conditions the soft parts of animals may be fossilized. This happens if the animal is caught in a material that prevents decay. Insects and other small animals may be preserved in the resin that oozes from pine trees; this resin may then become fossilized as amber. The conditions on the bottom of some seas, like the Black Sea today, prevent decay. We have found rocks, formed from the mud in these seas, that contain impressions of soft-bodied animals like jellyfish. In the ice of Siberia we have found mammoths which have been "deep frozen." The intense cold has stopped decay, and the animals are completely preserved.

Other kinds of fossils may be imprints of things like leaves or worms, or trails, or footprints, or burrows, or the marks of teeth, or even preserved excrement, which is called coprolite. All these can tell us about the animals and plants of the past.

In the next two chapters we will follow the history

This nest of dinosaur eggs was discovered in Mongolia. If conditions are right, even such delicate objects as these may become fossils.

of animal life from its beginnings. Here let us see the outlines of this picture.

At first, life was all in the sea. The very early animals we know nothing about. We can guess that they were small, simple, and without hard parts. Gradually, some animals grew bigger and more complicated: some developed shells; others had a hard outside and jointed legs; many were wormlike.

All these early animals were invertebrates – animals without backbones. The backboned animals come into our picture much later on, about 500 million years ago. The first fishlike animals were small creatures that probably lived in rivers.

At this time, the lands were still lifeless. Plants were the first living things to invade the land, but once they were there, animals also could come on land and eat them. The first fossil land animals are about 420 million years old – millipedes and scorpions.

The first backboned animals on land were certain fishes that lived in shallow water. In times of drought, these fishes could survive on land, for they had air bladders that could be used as lungs. From these fish came the amphibians, which dominated the land for millions of years. Then one group of them evolved so that they were more efficient land animals. These were the reptiles; and they spread quickly.

The reptiles were the lords of the earth for 200 million years. From them have come the two groups of backboned animals that are dominant on earth today: birds in the air and mammals on land.

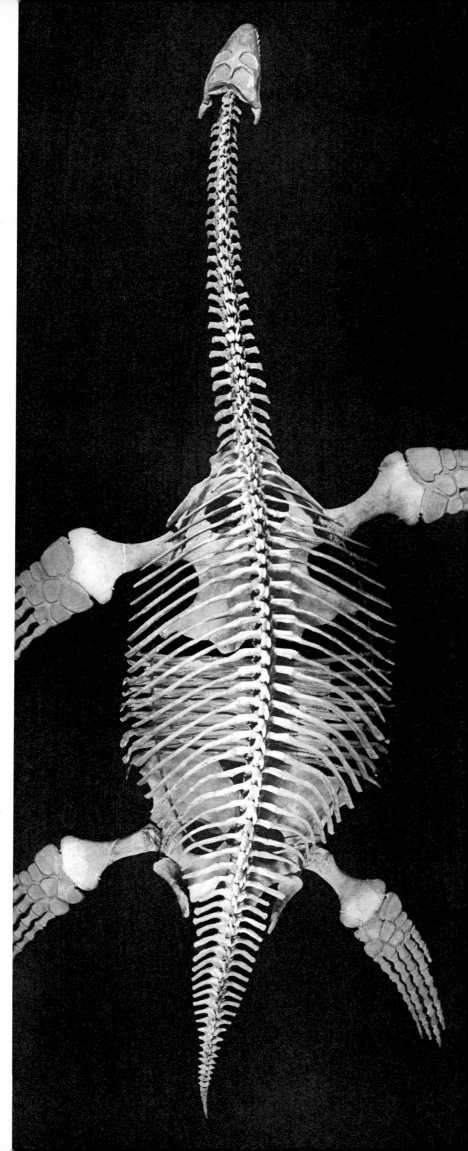

Fossil tracks, skin impressions and eggs are rare. Most fossils are of skeletons only – bones, teeth, shells, etc. All the soft parts of this fossilized ammonite have disappeared; and only the bones of this plesiosaur (right), a sea reptile, were preserved and remain as fossils.

In Arizona, U.S., the Colorado River has cut over a mile deep into the rocks and formed the Grand Canyon, a natural geological museum.

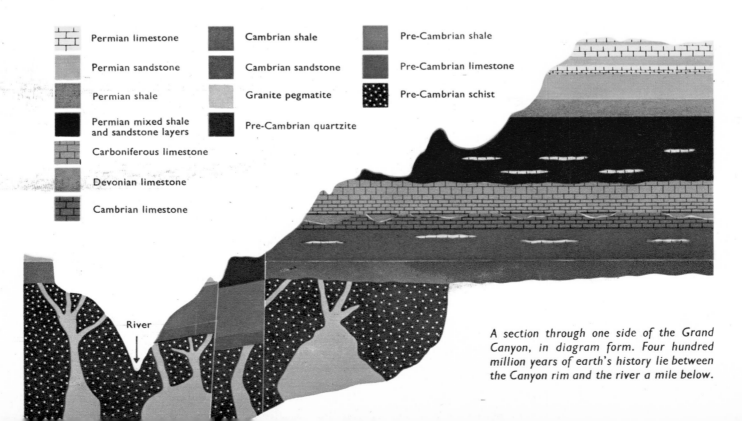

Permian limestone

Permian sandstone

Permian shale

Permian mixed shale and sandstone layers

Carboniferous limestone

Devonian limestone

Cambrian limestone

Cambrian shale

Cambrian sandstone

Granite pegmatite

Pre-Cambrian quartzite

Pre-Cambrian shale

Pre-Cambrian limestone

Pre-Cambrian schist

River

A section through one side of the Grand Canyon, in diagram form. Four hundred million years of earth's history lie between the Canyon rim and the river a mile below.

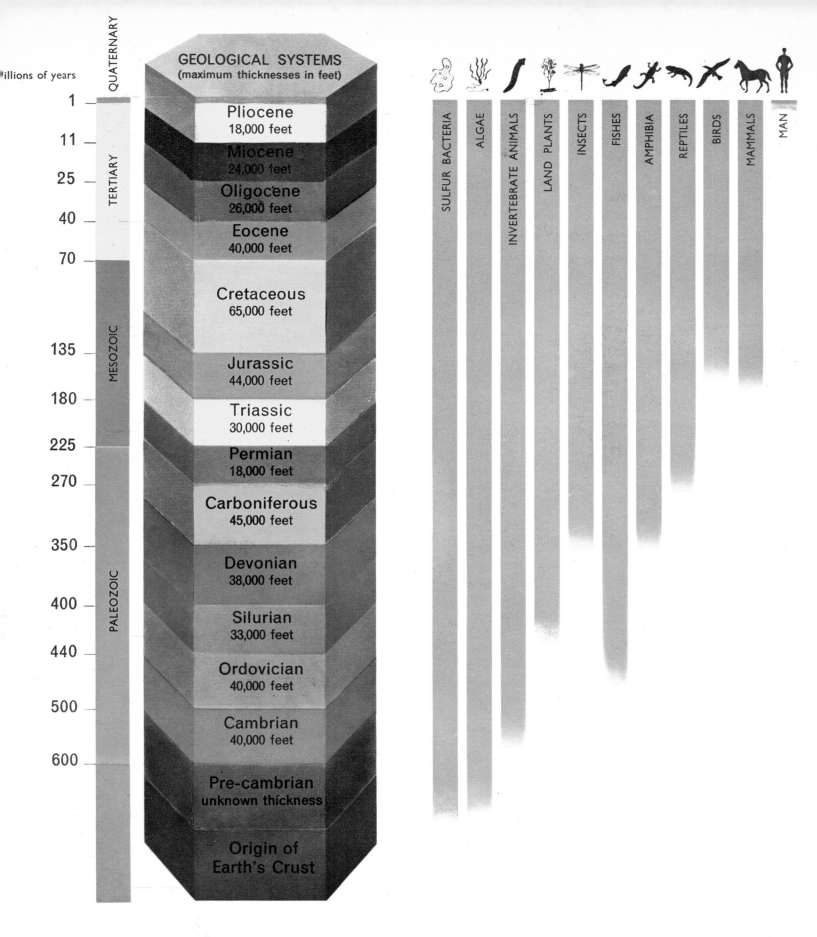

GEOLOGICAL SYSTEMS
(maximum thicknesses in feet)

Millions of years

QUATERNARY

TERTIARY

MESOZOIC

PALEOZOIC

	Pliocene	18,000 feet
	Miocene	24,000 feet
	Oligocene	26,000 feet
	Eocene	40,000 feet
	Cretaceous	65,000 feet
	Jurassic	44,000 feet
	Triassic	30,000 feet
	Permian	18,000 feet
	Carboniferous	45,000 feet
	Devonian	38,000 feet
	Silurian	33,000 feet
	Ordovician	40,000 feet
	Cambrian	40,000 feet

Pre-cambrian
unknown thickness

Origin of
Earth's Crust

1
11
25
40
70
135
180
225
270
350
400
440
500
600

SULFUR BACTERIA ALGAE INVERTEBRATE ANIMALS LAND PLANTS INSECTS FISHES AMPHIBIA REPTILES BIRDS MAMMALS MAN

The age of our planet is about 4600 million years. This diagram shows the last 600 million years, the stretch of time in which nearly all known fossils were formed. We divide this time into periods, much as we have Tudor and Stuart periods in English history. The big column on this page shows these periods, and the total thickness of the rock layers belonging to each. Not all the layers have been found in one country, but by matching layers in one place with those in another we have been able to work out a complete series. On the left are shown the Eras to which these periods belong: Paleozoic Era – age of ancient life; Mesozoic Era – age of middle life; Tertiary (third) and Quaternary (fourth) Eras together form the age of recent life. Time before the Paleozoic Era began (more than 600 million years ago) is called the Pre-Cambrian. The blue columns on the right show when various groups of living things arose.

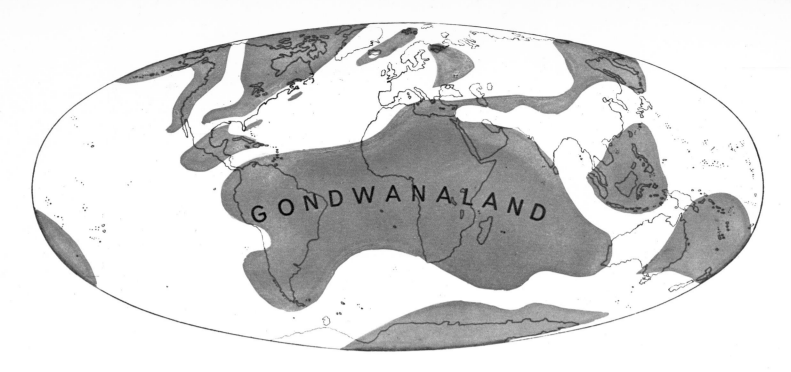

The Pageant of Life

Let us trace the story of animal life we have learned from the rocks.

We have no fossils of the earliest forms of life. Nor can we expect to find any, because the first living things must have been very small and soft. We think that these early forms of life arose in the sea, perhaps about 3000 million years ago or more.

The first evidence of life that we have found in the rocks is more than 2600 million years old. It is not a definite fossil, but consists of lumps made of thin layers of carbonate of lime. Much the same sort of lumps are made at the present time by water plants called blue-green algae. So these ancient lumps may be the remains of primitive sea plants.

The rocks in which we have found these lumps were formed in the Pre-Cambrian time (look back to the time chart on page 25). Pre-Cambrian rocks cover much of northwest Scotland, and parts of Norway and North America. Many are igneous rocks and so do not contain fossils. Most of the Pre-Cambrian sedimentary rocks have been so folded and squashed that their fossils have been destroyed.

But, despite this, a few Pre-Cambrian fossils have survived. In Canada, the rocks have revealed the remains of simple plants: limy deposits that once surrounded blue-green algae; and the threads and spores of fungi, lowly plants like modern molds and mushrooms. Rocks in the United States and Canada show other traces of early life: burrows that may have been made by worms; impressions of animals akin to sponges, and even the imprint of a jellyfish.

From fragments such as these, and what we know about the life of simple animals today, we can build up a picture of early life. We know that all life in the Pre-Cambrian was in the sea. At that time there was nothing on the land; nothing but rain beating on the rocks, heat from the sun, and sometimes snow and ice.

Floating in the sea there must have been many millions of tiny plants and animals, as there still are today. As life evolved, some animals took to crawling along the sea floor; small flatworms first, later many different types of worm, some of which started to burrow in the mud. Other animals, like sea anemones and sponges, lived fixed to the rocks.

By the end of the Pre-Cambrian there must have been swimming animals; some rather like shrimps. Then there must have been the first shelled animals: lamp shells which had two horny shells, and mollusks whose bodies were partly protected by limy shells.

During the Pre-Cambrian, then, a variety of living things evolved from the first few forms. Though we have so little fossil evidence of this life, we know that it must have existed because at the beginning of the next period of time, the Cambrian, we find fossils of many different kinds of animal.

Some lumps of Pre-Cambrian limestone when split (as in photograph above, 1½ times natural size) show layers of limy deposits. These may be the remains of simple plants which were surrounded by limy cases; and if so, are among the very few Pre-Cambrian fossils.

Below: this fossil of a curious little animal called Xenusion (here enlarged 2 times) was found in late Pre-Cambrian sandstone. It seems to be a fossil of an animal half way between a worm and an arthropod, and is one of the best Pre-Cambrian fossils found so far.

Cambrian sea life

Imagine we were peering through the window of a submarine time-machine. Life 600 million years ago must have looked something like this. In the reconstruction the colors are guesswork but the shapes are not. Living fixed to the bottom there are seaweeds (1), and several sorts of sponge (2-5), on the rocks are hard parts (spicules) of dead sponges (6-7). Moving slowly over the sea floor are both spiny worms (8) and various other worms (9-10), some of which live in burrows in the sand. We see echinoderms fixed by a stalk (11), and flat ones (12) and a sea cucumber creeping slowly along (13). A strange little animal — an onychophoran that is possibly a relative of *Xenusion* of Pre-Cambrian times — runs past on its many pairs of legs (14). Swimming and crawling round us there are several kinds of trilobite (15-18), some quite large. We catch sight of a crustacean with a large bivalve shell (19), and see a shrimplike one hurry by (20). In the water above, a shoal of jellyfish drifts past (21).

There are fossils of all these animals in the Burgess shales (see p. 30). In these rocks the fossils are so well preserved that even details of the organs of soft-bodied animals can be made out.

Life in the sea 600 million years ago was not all that different from life in the sea today. If we went below a present-day sea in an observation submarine we would of course find many newer types; but we could also see members of all the groups in this reconstruction — except for trilobites, which are now all extinct, and the onychophoran whose descendants now live on land.

Cambrian—600 million years ago

The Cambrian is the first period in the Paleozoic Era – the age of ancient life. It began, we now think, about 600 million years ago and lasted for about 100 million years. In this great stretch of time living things developed in many ways.

The rocks of Cambrian age were first studied in Wales more than 100 years ago. This is why it is called the Cambrian, for *Cambria* was the Latin name for Wales. Cambrian rocks have since been discovered in many other parts of the world. Much of the eastern United States (the Appalachian region) and Canada is covered with Cambrian rocks.

At the beginning of the Cambrian there were long, cold, almost ice age, spells, but later on the climate seems to have become warmer. Wind-worn pebbles in Texas and Wisconsin in the United States suggest that some places were dry, and even desertlike, at this time.

In Cambrian rocks we find the first good fossils; in places quite a number of them. Compared with the Pre-Cambrian animals, far more Cambrian animals had hard parts, like shells. These had a much greater chance of being preserved than the soft bodies of Pre-Cambrian animals. Also, many of these animals with hard parts grew to be quite large, several inches to a foot long, because the hard parts could support a body this size.

Why did so many of these animals develop hard parts at this time? A suggested answer is that some types of animal became hunters, and the animals they hunted could survive only if they had tough protective coverings.

We know quite a bit about some of the soft-bodied animals of the Cambrian because of a very exceptional set of fossils that were found near Field, in Canada. These fossils are in rocks called Burgess shales, which were formed at the bottom of a very stagnant sea. This sea, we think, was like the Black Sea is today. Conditions along the bottom of the Black Sea are so unsuitable for living things that no bacteria (which usually play the major part in destroying the bodies of dead animals) or scavenging animals can live there. The bodies of dead animals are therefore hardly disturbed.

So, in the ancient sea where the Burgess shales were formed, the dead animals that drifted to the bottom were covered with mud before they decayed. In these rocks we have found fossils of jellyfish, worms, sponges, starfish and many other sea animals,

all wonderfully preserved. Even the internal parts of some of them can be studied. This lucky chance has told us a lot about these animals.

The picture on pages 28-29 shows what life on a sea floor in Cambrian times might have looked like. In this picture there are many kinds of animals belonging to groups of which some members are alive today. But other Cambrian animals are quite unfamiliar to us: they belong to groups which are now extinct, that is, have all died out.

The Graptolites were one of these now-extinct groups. The name graptolite comes from the Greek words which mean "written stone," because fossil graptolites look like pencil markings on slates. Graptolites had branching rods that held lots of little cups in each of which a simple animal lived. The cups were all interconnected, so that the living animal was a series of one-roomed houses attached to a float. The fossil graptolites we find are the remnants of the cups, rods and branches.

The fossils we find most often in Cambrian rocks belong to another extinct group, the Trilobites. These had, as their name suggests, three lobes: a central part, with a lobe on either side.

Trilobites look like oval pieces of venetian blind because their body was divided up into segments. These segments allowed the animal to roll up into a ball, except for its head. On the underside of each segment there was a pair of two-part jointed legs, one part being for walking, the other for swimming and perhaps for breathing.

Many trilobites probably crawled around over the mud of the sea bottom, searching for their food of dead and dying animals. Some of these scavenging trilobites were blind.

Trilobites were mostly about an inch long, but some were so small they can be seen only with a microscope, and others were as much as 18 inches long. They are classified in the group of animals called arthropods, and so are very distant relations of the crabs, shrimps and insects.

Life in the seas in the Cambrian was thus much like life in the seas today; although the animals that played the various parts of hunter and hunted, and that swam or floated or remained fixed, were quite different from the animals that play these parts now.

The land was another thing. During the Cambrian, no living creature had ventured onto the land, and none would for 60 million more years – at least we do not find traces of land life until that time.

Trilobites are the commonest Cambrian fossils. This one is only two inches long.

Below: one half of a Cambrian lamp shell.

This fossil is an impression of a worm made in the mud of a Cambrian sea bed.

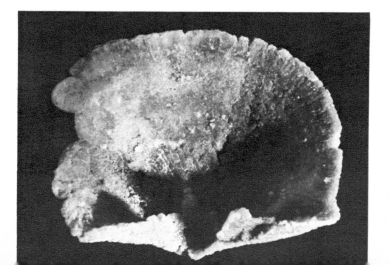

Ordovician—500 million years ago

Ordovician rocks were also first studied in Wales: so the early geologists named the period after the Ordovices, a tribe who once lived in western Wales. Ordovician rocks occur in many other parts of the world and cover great areas of the United States and Canada.

Life was still all in the seas and these seas seem to have covered much the same parts of the world as Cambrian seas (see map on page 26).

Many of the animals of the Ordovician were not much different from their ancestors of the Cambrian. Trilobites were at their most numerous: hundreds of fossil species are known from all over the world in Ordovician rocks. Graptolites were common, and also lamp shells.

A striking feature of life in the Ordovician was the development of the mollusks. Several types of Cambrian mollusk are known, but in the Ordovician some groups rivaled the trilobites in number and importance. There were bivalves, like the clams and oysters of today. And there were the one-shelled gastropods, both those like limpets, and coiled-shell ones like whelks.

Perhaps the most interesting mollusks were the

Below: Nautilus is a modern cephalopod. This diagram shows its body (red) is inside its shell (blue) while its head and "arms" stick out of shell opening. Shell has been partly cut away to show empty chambers (yellow) which animal has outgrown. Small diagrams show shapes of some fossil cephalopods. Right: the fossil shell of a coiled Ordovician cephalopod, called Lituites.

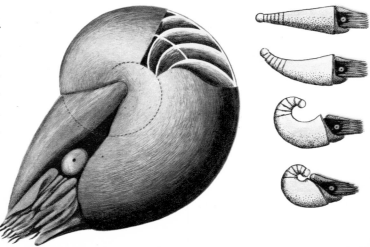

In Ordovician seas there were many cephalopods, some with straight shells (1), some with coiled ones (2). Other types of mollusk were whelklike gastropods (3) and bivalves (4). In this reconstruction we also see trilobites, both swimming kinds (5) and crawling kinds (6); starfish (7), sea urchins (8) and echinoderms with stalks (9-10); lamp shells (11-12); moss animals (13-14); a bushlike graptolite (15) and one like a tuning-fork (16); cup corals (17) and a coral colony (18); sponges (19). At the back, sea lilies wave their long arms (20), and an ostracoderm lies on the mud of the sea floor (21).

cephalopods, a name which means " head-foot," for part of their muscular foot was divided into " arms " that surrounded the animal's head as it stuck out of its shell. There are few cephalopods left today but in the past this group was enormously successful. Most of them had shells, which contained a series of chambers. When the cephalopod was young it lived in a little simple shell. As it grew bigger it moved out of this and made a new chamber around itself, but the first shell was still attached at the end. As it grew larger and larger it moved again and again, but still it carried with it all its old houses.

Some tiny scraps of fossils from Colorado in the United States are more important to us than all the other Ordovician fossils. They are the earliest remains of animals with bone, the animals we call vertebrates (meaning " backboned "), a group that includes man himself, as well as other mammals, birds, reptiles, amphibians and fish.

These important fossils were found in a bed of rock that was formed either in an estuary or in fresh water. But they are so few, and such little scraps, they are difficult to understand. In the next period, the Silurian, we find much better fossils of these, our far-distant ancestors.

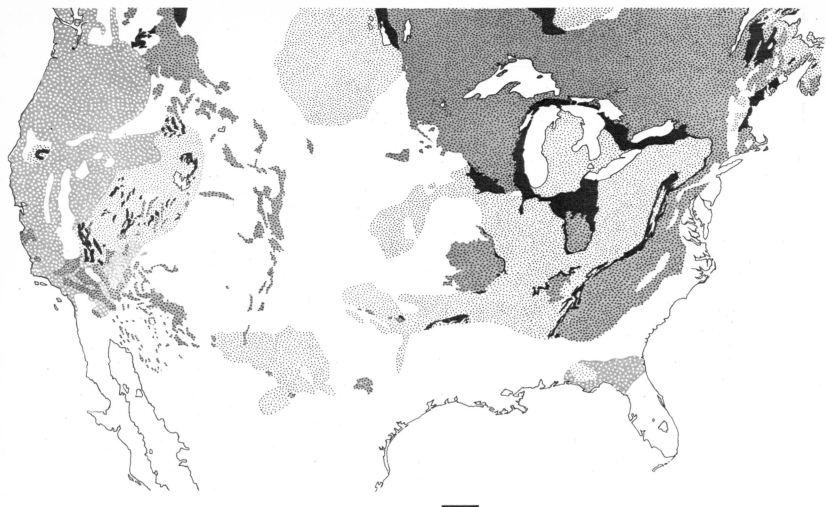

Silurian—440 million years ago

Silurian rocks are found in many parts of the British Isles, in Northern Europe, and in many places in North America (see map above). But again, rocks of this period were first studied in Wales, where they are the rocks at the surface in many places, and so the period was called after another Welsh tribe, the Silures.

These rocks were all formed in seas that must have been very much alike, for we have found fossils of the same animals in the United States and on the Swedish island called Gotland. On the whole, the Silurian seems to have been a time of mild and even temperatures. At the end of the period, which lasted for about 40 million years, vigorous earth movements started to form new mountain ranges.

What kind of changes were there in the life of the Silurian? In the seas there was little change. Lamp shells were so common in some shallow waters that their shells made shell beaches. Among the echinoderms there were forms that lived fixed to the bottom by a tall stalk and wafted food into their mouths with their waving arms; these are called sea lilies.

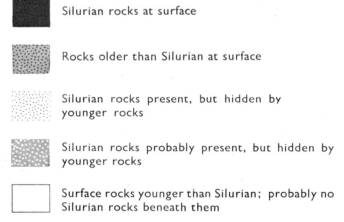

Silurian rocks at surface

Rocks older than Silurian at surface

Silurian rocks present, but hidden by younger rocks

Silurian rocks probably present, but hidden by younger rocks

Surface rocks younger than Silurian; probably no Silurian rocks beneath them

But in the estuaries, shallow coastal waters and in the rivers, we see great developments. In these waters lived the little primitive fishlike animals we first saw in the Ordovician.

We have many quite well preserved fossils of these in Silurian rocks. The first ones had no jaws and most had some form of armor. In fact their name, Ostracoderm, means "shell-skinned." Some had a covering shell of bone over their heads, and scaly bodies; others had close rows of scales all down

Ostracoderms, like the one in this reconstruction, were vertebrates. They had a bony skeleton inside their body as well as outside armor.

their bodies. As they had no jaws, these little animals, we think, must have been scavengers, or have filtered off tiny bits of food from the water with their gills, which were very large.

Because they had bone, we know that the ostracoderms were vertebrates. We can picture these ancestors of ours as grubbing around in the mud of shallow waters, harmless creatures depending on their armor to protect them.

Perhaps the animals the little ostracoderms feared most were the Eurypterids – the largest animals of the Silurian. One kind was nine feet long! The eurypterids are related to the scorpions of modern times and so are sometimes called sea scorpions. All the eurypterids died out long ago, but we have some very good fossils of them. Their bodies were divided into a number of segments and they had several pairs of limbs, including a large pair of paddles. These sea scorpions were probably both hunters and scavengers.

The eurypterids were arthropods, which all have a basic body plan that is quite different from that of a vertebrate. A vertebrate has a skeleton, usually of bone, inside its body, though it may have an outside protective skeleton as well, as a tortoise does. But arthropods have only an outside skeleton, and this is of a horny material called chitin. There are many other differences between these two groups, which are the most complicated of all animals. In the Silurian, the arthropods were large and dominated

The hard outside skeleton of this eurypterid has been preserved as a fossil. As it was an arthropod, it had no skeleton inside its body.

The Silurian fossil Jaymoytius (reconstruction above), discovered in Scotland, was, perhaps, a relation of the very early vertebrates.

the vertebrates. In later ages, as we shall see, the vertebrates became the most important animals on earth, dominating all other living things.

Toward the end of the Silurian, the vertebrates were already developing. New types arose that had jaws and so could bite, not just nibble. These Placoderms, the first true fish, were already fishlike in shape; they had several pairs of fins down their body and probably could swim well.

So far, the story of life has been a story confined to water. In the Silurian we have our first glimpses of life on land. In early ages the lands were bare; but as time went on the heat, the cold, the rain and the wind broke up the hard rock, as they do today. Eventually soil, soft and suitable for plants to grow in, was formed.

The first life on land must have been plant life. All animals, in the end, depend on plants for their food. This is because plants can make their food from water, the gas carbon dioxide, and salts. They use the energy of sunlight to do this, and need the green pigment called chlorophyll. (Chlorophyll is what makes plants green.) But animals cannot do this; they must eat ready-made food. So, before animals could live wholly on the land, plants had to be there first.

We could not expect many fossils of the first land plants, but we have found traces of plants in Silurian rocks from Europe and from Australia which show that some plants had managed the great move to the land. The plants that did so, quickly spread and evolved into many forms, for they were in a place where they had no competitors.

From Scotland, in late Silurian rocks, we have the first evidence that animals had come on land too; only traces, but recognizable as millipedes and scorpions. These, so far as we yet know, were the first air breathers.

Our Silurian scene shows both land and sea, for at this time lived the first land plants – psilopsids (reconstruction at left) – and the first land animals such as scorpions (1) and millipedes (2). In the sea are cephalopods (3, 4, 5); whelklike mollusks (6, 7), and a bivalve shell (8); a trilobite (9), a brittle-star (10), and sea lilies (11, 12); lamp shells (13); a worm (14); graptolites (15, 16) and a colony of moss animals (17). Corals grow fixed to rocks, both cup corals (18) and many of the reef-forming ones (19, 20, 21, 22); stromatoporoids (23), small animals living in colonies enclosed in joined skeletons like the reef-forming corals, also helped make reefs. A newcomer is an eurypterid (24). Perhaps in a scene like this we might also expect an ostracoderm (25).

Devonian—400 million years ago

In the Devonian, the fish came into their own; indeed we can call this period the age of fish, for their fossils are very abundant in the rocks of this period – some small, others enormous; some heavily armored like their Silurian ancestors, some covered with small scales; some fast swimming and shark-like, others slow and sluggish.

But the empire of the fish was not confined to the water. In the Devonian, some fish first ventured out of the water to live part of their lives on land.

Thus the Devonian was a time of great change. And not only in the animals. All through the period earth movements were building new mountains. It was a time when sudden torrential rains fell, then the hot sun dried up the lands until some were deserts.

From the sharp peaks of the new mountains, a vast amount of material was carried away by these heavy rains. The rivers bore this down to inland waters and seas, and dropped it there in great deltas. This material became Old Red Sandstones.

In deeper waters, thick layers of mud gathered. Today we find this mud as slates and shales. Large parts of the counties of Devon and Cornwall, in the southwest corner of England, are made of these dark rocks. That is why we call this time the Devonian.

What sorts of animal lived in Devonian seas? Let us start with the invertebrates. In many places we find coral reefs. These are great stretches of limy rock: the remains of millions and millions of limy houses made by little coral animals.

Many different types of lamp shell flourished in the Devonian. In fact, their fossils are so common we can use them to mark the different rock layers.

Devonian seas must have swarmed with mollusks for we find many fossils of them, particularly the coiled cephalopods. We also find lots of other invertebrates, like sponges, sea lilies, starfish and eurypterids. But some types of animal we find less often than in previous periods. There were far fewer trilobites in the Devonian; they were no longer an important part of sea life. And the graptolites, too,

This giant is Dinichthys – *a 30-foot long Devonian placoderm. With it are some early sharks. More Devonian fish are shown opposite:* Cladoselache – *a shark;* Climatius, Pterichthyodes *and* Coccosteus – *placoderms;* Osteolepis – *a lobe-fin; and* Cheirolepis – *a ray-fin.*

were slowly dying out, soon to vanish altogether.

More important than any of these, we repeat, are the fish. In Devonian rocks we find fossils of four main sorts of fish. First, there were still ostracoderms. Then there were the armored placoderms. Some of these grew to enormous sizes: *Dinichthys* was probably 30 feet long.

Third, there were the ancestors of our sharks and rays. This group is unlike other fish in many ways. Their skeleton is not bone, but a transparent hard material called cartilage. The early members of this group, like *Cladoselache*, were already shark-shaped. They had many sharp teeth and were hunters.

The fourth type of fish we find in the Devonian were the ancestors of most of the animals we now think of as fish. We find these bony fish both in seas and in fresh waters. There were two groups of them.

One group, the ray-fins, had a great many bony rods supporting their fins (that is why these fish are called "ray-fins"). But the other group, the lobe-fins and lungfish, had a fleshy lobe at the body end of

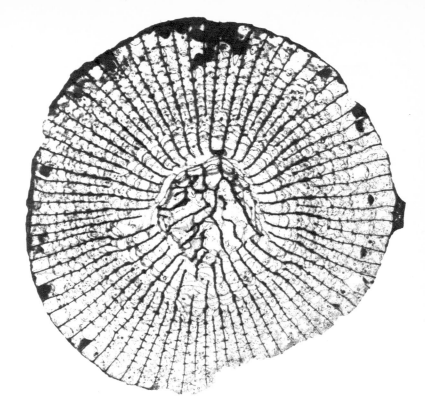

In the Devonian we find lots of corals: solitary ones with cuplike skeletons (this fossil was photographed from above, looking down into the cup); and colonial ones, whose skeletons formed reefs.

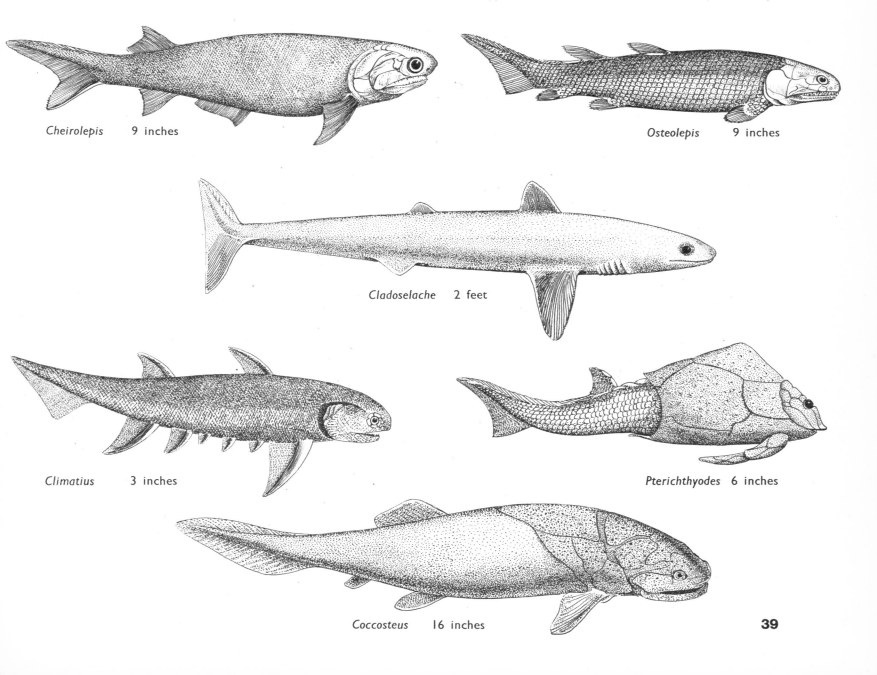

Cheirolepis   9 inches

Osteolepis   9 inches

Cladoselache   2 feet

Climatius   3 inches

Pterichthyodes   6 inches

Coccosteus   16 inches

Cheirolepis

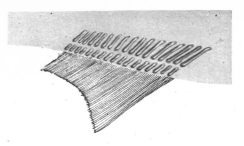

Eusthenopteron

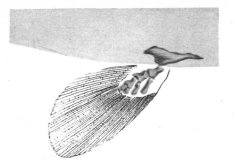

Eryops

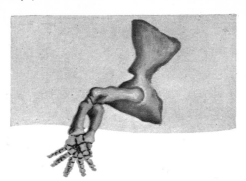

In Devonian lakes and rivers lived both ray-finned and lobe-finned fish. Cheirolepis was a ray-fin; Eusthenopteron was a lobe-fin. The diagrams above show the difference between the bones that supported their fins.

Cheirolepis

Eusthenopteron

their fins, and in this lobe were a few large bones. Such a fin is strong and can be twisted and turned into many positions.

The Devonian lobe-fins lived in rivers. But in the uncertain climate of those times, a river might not remain a river. In the many droughts some must have become thin streams and others must have dried up altogether leaving only a few muddy ponds.

What happened to the fish in these rivers? Most of them must have died in the droughts. But the lobe-fins had a chance of survival. As well as gills, they had an air bladder which they could use as a lung and so they could live out of water for a little while, and they could pull themselves along on land with their strong fins. Perhaps as the rivers dried up, a few lobe-fins struggled out of their particular pool as it shrank away, and painfully dragged themselves to a deeper part of the river where a patch of water still remained. Thus the first vertebrate to walk on land was searching for more water!

Clumsy as they were, these first land vertebrates must have begun to find the land a good place to live. For by the end of the Devonian we find a few fossil traces of four-legged, not four-finned, vertebrates – the amphibians, a name which means " two ways of life," for they could live both on land and in water.

A few fossil amphibian bones come from Greenland, which was probably a warm, swampy place in the Devonian. And we have found a single footprint in Devonian rocks in Pennyslvania that tells us that an amphibian passed that way, though we know nothing more about this animal.

These lumbering, fishlike amphibians were not the only animals on Devonian lands. The invertebrates, as we saw, invaded the land in the Silurian. Now we find, as well as millipedes and scorpions, spiders and the first insects, which had no wings.

What kinds of plants provided shelter for these land animals? The warm climate allowed the slender plants of the Silurian to develop enormously. Suddenly, it seems, we find horsetail rushes, and tall feathery tree ferns, some of which were so large their stems were more than three feet thick. Scale trees, called after their scaly trunks, grew to 40 feet high in the swamps. So the world's first forests grew during the Devonian.

Amphibians, like Eryops (below), came from lobe-fin fishes. There are many resemblances between lobe-fins like Eusthenopteron and early amphibians. One of the most important is shown in the diagrams at left. Unlike the ray-fins, such as Cheirolepis, which had many small bones supporting their fins, Eusthenopteron and other lobe-fins had a few large bones in the base of their fins. The leg bones of an amphibian, even a later one like Eryops, are arranged in much the same way.

The modern Australian lungfish also has a lobed fin similar to that of Eusthenopteron. The pictures on the right, drawn from a living lungfish, show how this type of fin can be twisted in many directions.

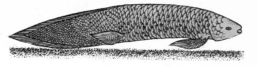
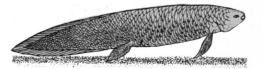
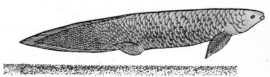
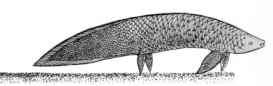
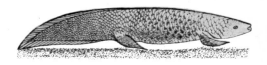

Eryops

What is now Greenland may have looked much like this in the late Devonian – a warm swamp. These animals, called Ichthyostega, are the earliest amphibians we have found as fossils. They were still partly fishlike; for instance, they had bony rays supporting their tail fins.

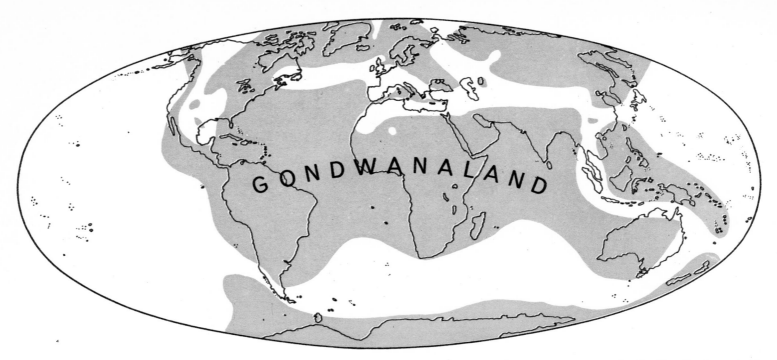

In the lower Carboniferous, much of the world was land (brown in map above); the only major ocean was the Pacific. Gondwanaland had extended until it covered most of Australia, parts of south Asia and most of the Atlantic. Compare with Cambrian map, page 26.

Carboniferous—350 million years ago

Though our story is about prehistoric animals, in this period we will pay a lot of attention to plants. For in the later part of the Carboniferous, great forests grew over much of the Northern Hemisphere. Today, we find the remains of these forests as coal; our major source of power for so long. This coal gives the period its name: Carboniferous means "carbon-bearing," and coal is mostly carbon.

The Carboniferous falls into two parts, and in America the two halves have different names: the lower Carboniferous is called the Mississippian; the upper Carboniferous, the Pennsylvanian. The world must have changed quite a lot between the two halves for their characteristic rocks are quite different.

The map on this page shows what the world looked like in the lower Carboniferous, about 350 million years ago. In the many clear shallow seas, the water contained much lime. This left limy muds that we find now as limestones, the characteristic rocks of the lower Carboniferous.

Swimming and crawling in these seas were many kinds of mollusks; cephalopods, mostly coiled ones; bivalves; gastropods; and sometimes chitons, the "coat-of-mail" shells.

There were so many of these mollusks that we find reefs of them, together with lamp shells, lime-covered seaweeds, and moss animals. We find corals, too, but these were mostly solitary – not the reef builders

that we saw in the Devonian. Sea lilies waved their long arms from the sea floor. And there were still eurypterids.

Preserved in Carboniferous rocks are lots of teeth and fin spines, the only remnants we have of the many sharks that lived at this time. The bony fish, called enamel scales, had heavier scales than their modern descendants, but otherwise would not look too strange to our eyes.

In the lower Carboniferous, we have only traces of fossil amphibians, parts of skulls and skeletons, and some footprints. But from the coal deposits, formed in the swampy forests of the upper Carboniferous we have good fossils of land animals.

What is coal and how is it made? Coal is the fossil remains of plants. In the swampy forests, the dying trees fell into the stagnant water. There they did not rot away completely. Instead, they were slowly pressed into a mass with the leaves, branches, mud and other debris that fell on top of them, until they became peat. In time, chemical changes in this peat, and more pressure, turned it first into soft brown coals, and eventually after millions of years, into the hard black stuff we burn in our fires.

At the time these forests grew, much of Europe and North America was low-lying land. Throughout the upper Carboniferous, the land slowly sank and then rose again, alternately. So the low swamps would be flooded by sea for many thousands of years; but

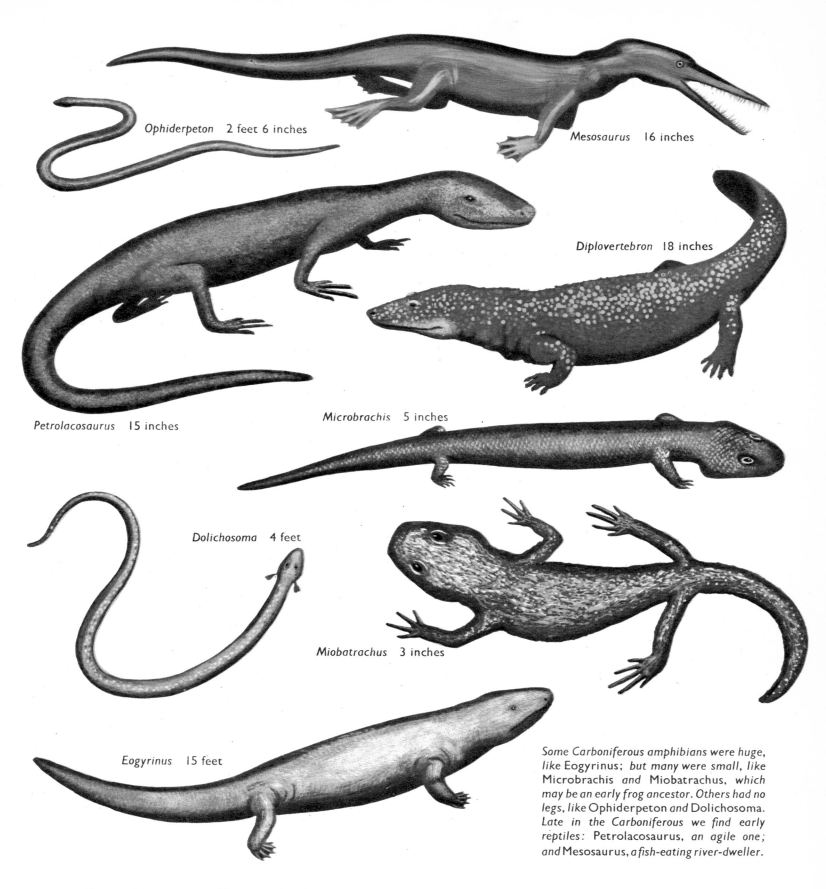

Ophiderpeton 2 feet 6 inches

Mesosaurus 16 inches

Diplovertebron 18 inches

Petrolacosaurus 15 inches

Microbrachis 5 inches

Dolichosoma 4 feet

Miobatrachus 3 inches

Eogyrinus 15 feet

Some Carboniferous amphibians were huge, like Eogyrinus; *but many were small, like* Microbrachis and Miobatrachus, *which may be an early frog ancestor. Others had no legs, like* Ophiderpeton *and* Dolichosoma. *Late in the Carboniferous we find early reptiles:* Petrolacosaurus, *an agile one; and* Mesosaurus, *a fish-eating river-dweller.*

eventually would rise up and become land again; then trees would spread over this new land. Thus the seams of coal that are mined today are often separated by layers of rock that were laid down in these warm shallow seas.

A coal forest was not like any of the forests we know. Instead of oaks, maples or fir trees, there were tall tree ferns, scale trees, and giant horsetails like *Calamites*. Under these great trees, some of which were as much as 100 feet high, there were seed ferns,

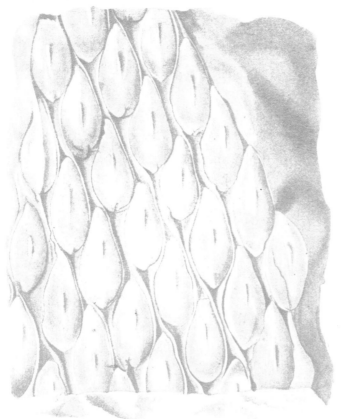

ordinary ferns, and many small rushes and horsetails. None of these had flowers, but many had cones which were probably brightly colored.

The upper Carboniferous in Europe and North America was a warm damp time; winter and summer must have been alike, for the tree trunks do not have annual rings – the lines that in modern trees show the great growth in our warm spring and summer after the cold winter. A Carboniferous forest must have looked the same, year in year out; for the trees in it dropped their leaves one by one, as a fir tree does, not all at once like an oak.

In the steamy damp of these forests were many small animals that would be quite familiar to us: snails, spiders, scorpions, centipedes and hundreds of different kinds of cockroach.

Among the insects, dragonflies were common; one kind, called *Meganeura*, measured 30 inches from wing-tip to wing-tip.

Splashing in the swampy pools were lungfish, enamel scales, and even king crabs, whose descendants now live only in the sea. But the most interesting inhabitants of these pools were the amphibians. Some were small and newtlike. Others were long, slim snakelike animals that had no legs. Others were as large as crocodiles. Some lived all their lives in water. Others dwelt mainly on the banks. Many had hard scaly skins, unlike the soft little amphibians we know.

We can picture these sprawling creatures slithering among the fallen trees, as they crossed from pool to pool, catching lungfish and the little enamel scales, snapping at great insects, nosing out a cockroach from under a log, and crunching up a king crab.

Amphibians were the only backboned animals on Carboniferous lands for a while. Then one group of them started to change into a new sort of animal – reptiles. Reptiles are more successful land animals than amphibians in many ways. The most important difference is in their eggs. Amphibians lay their eggs in water, surrounded by a soft jelly. But reptiles lay eggs on land that are enclosed in a firm protective shell, each with its own supply of water inside.

We do not know when or where the important changes occurred that slowly made a reptile from an amphibian, but probably it was early in the Carboniferous. For in late Carboniferous rocks we find truly reptilian skeletons, and in the next period, the Permian, we find many developments in this new way of life – life away from water.

In swampy Carboniferous forests lived amphibians like Diplovertebron (front) and 15-foot Eogyrinus (behind). Tall scale trees (left front and in background) and tree ferns grew there. Giant horsetails (in front), ferns and seed ferns clothed the ground and huge dragonflies, like Meganeura, flew in the damp air. Fossils shown here (from top to bottom); a scale tree branch, and the bark pattern of another; a fernlike leaf; and a two-inch long insect.

Permian—270 million years ago

The Permian, called after the Perm region in Russia, is the end of the Age of Ancient Life. The 45 million years of this period were a time of great change. Many of the old forms of life died out completely during the Permian and new, more modern, types arose to take their place.

The earth was still in the throes of great movements. Volcanoes spewed forth lava and ash, and new mountain ranges were thrown up. In the Northern Hemisphere these changes sometimes cut off arms of the sea. In hot dry places the land-locked seas began to dry up. As they did so, the water in them became more and more salty, and life became difficult, if not impossible, for the animals living in these seas.

Other Permian rocks, red ones, tell us again that this was a hot dry time over much of the north. But in the Southern Hemisphere, the great continent of Gondwanaland was in the grip of an ice age. The high flat lands were covered with an ice cap, as Greenland is today. From this huge mass of ice, glaciers spread out over the lower-lying land. Even places in the tropics were cold then.

What was life like in Permian seas? Ammonites, coiled cephalopods, were common and can be used to mark the different rock layers. In this period we find the last traces of the trilobites that we first saw 330 million years before, at the beginning of the Cambrian. The eurypterids, too, make their last appearance in this time.

The plants also were changing. Ferns, tree ferns and seed ferns were still growing abundantly but the scale trees and giant horsetails became smaller and less common. Instead, more and more of the trees were conifers; and by the end of the Permian, the forests were mostly of fir and pine trees.

What was happening to the vertebrates? The open seas were thronged with fish, both sharks and enamel

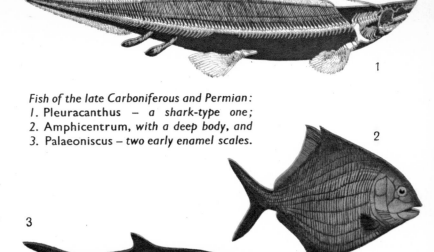

Fish of the late Carboniferous and Permian:
1. *Pleuracanthus* – a shark-type one;
2. *Amphicentrum*, with a deep body, and
3. *Palaeoniscus* – two early enamel scales.

scales. But the old placoderms, the first true fish, died out in the Permian.

In and around the lakes and rivers, the amphibians went their ways. Many were large strong animals, big enough to defend themselves against the attacks of their descendants, the reptiles. Some, like *Eryops*, had quite heavy bones, particularly in their skulls. Others had smaller, more delicate bones, and probably lived all their lives in water.

One of the most interesting Permian amphibians is called *Seymouria*. Its skeleton is part amphibian, part reptile. It was not an ancestor of the reptiles because it lived millions of years after we find fossils of undoubted reptiles. But it is interesting because it shows us that, as well as the ones that evolved into reptiles, there were some types of amphibians that became reptilelike.

True reptiles were found all over the place, living in a variety of ways. There were heavy beasts, like *Pareiasaurus*, which was nine feet long and moved its body on sprawling legs, and the smaller *Elginia* which had bony spikes on its skull. These clumsy reptiles

Eryops, a Permian amphibian that was almost entirely a land dweller, had strong legs, but still crawled along with its body near the ground.

obviously could not catch any fast-moving prey, and their large, grinding teeth tell us that they were plant-eaters.

Other reptiles were smaller and more agile. They must have been rather like lizards in many ways, and were probably insect-eaters, at least partly.

Some very interesting and important Permian reptiles were the fin-backed ones. They must have looked most extraordinary, for the spines of their backbones were enormously long. Over these tall spines a web of skin was stretched. No one knows what use this "sail" was: the best suggestion so far is that it was a radiator for getting rid of excess heat, for these reptiles lived in hot dry lands.

Some of the fin-backed reptiles were plant-eaters, like *Edaphosaurus*. Others, like *Dimetrodon*, were flesh-eaters. The fin-backs had teeth quite different from other reptiles. Reptiles usually have many teeth which are all the same – think of those of the modern crocodile. But *Dimetrodon* had short nipping front teeth, then a pair of large teeth and at the back a row of smaller ones. In fact, it had the same sort of tooth arrangement as a mammal has. So they are called mammal-like (theromorph) reptiles.

Later mammal-like reptiles had no great fins on their backs, but their teeth were even more varied. They were less clumsy than the fin-backs, and could run faster, for their legs were turned more underneath their bodies, instead of sprawling out sideways in the old amphibianlike way.

Thus in the Permian, the reptiles had begun to lay claim to the land. The heyday of the amphibians was over. In the next three periods, which together form the Middle Age of Life, the reptiles reach their peak in size and number, and on land, and in the sea and air dominated all other animals.

Dimetrodon, *a flesh-eating fin-backed reptile of the Permian,* chases a young Ophiacodon, *a cousin of the fin-backs which had no "sail." Notice Dimetrodon's varied teeth. In the background, another fin-back, called Edaphosaurus, collects its food – plants.*

Triassic—225 million years ago

The Triassic is the beginning of the Mesozoic, the Middle Age of Life. Through this Age we will trace the rise of the reptiles, their spread into many different ways of life, and at the end, their sudden descent into obscurity.

The name Triassic comes from Trias – meaning "three," for in Germany the early paleontologists found three totally different types of rock formed within the time of this period, which lasted for about 30 million years.

What was the world like in Triassic times? There were still two huge continents: Gondwanaland in the Southern Hemisphere, and a northern one covering much of what is now North America, the Atlantic Ocean, Great Britain, Europe and most of Russia. The continents were largely desert, with plains of shifting sands and pools that left salty deposits.

The life of Triassic seas looks at first glance much like that of previous periods. But if we examine it more closely we find that many of the invertebrate animals were more like their descendants of today than like the Paleozoic members of their groups. For instance, the Paleozoic corals had their body parts arranged in fours. But in the Triassic we first find corals with body parts in sixes, like modern corals. Triassic sea lilies, too, were like modern ones.

There were fewer lamp shells than before, but the gastropod and bivalve mollusks more than make up for this: we find them everywhere. Ammonites also flourished in the warm Triassic seas; but at the end of the period almost all of them mysteriously died out; though in the next period they were just as abundant again.

The bony fish were also slowly becoming more like modern ones. Their scales were not quite so thick as those of the Paleozoic enamel scales. There were many sorts of these bony fish – including the first flying fish.

In the pools and rivers we find lungfish; and the last of the great amphibians lumbered in and out of the fresh waters. Some of these Triassic forms were amongst the largest of all amphibians. *Paracyclotosaurus* measured nearly 10 feet; *Mastodonsaurus* had a head four feet long.

The Triassic rocks of Spitsbergen have shown us fossils of some very strange amphibians. These, like the long-snouted *Aphaneramma*, probably spent at least part of their adult life in the sea – a place where we never find amphibians now.

Above: in Cheshire, England, there are salt deposits, formed when inland seas dried up in hot Triassic lands. In these harsh places few animals could live. Pictured are early thecodont, and the trail of handlike footprints it left; also a rhynchocephalian reptile (front).

In the Triassic, the reptiles first became masters of the seas. The sea reptiles here are (from left to right): an ichthyosaur, Mixosaurus; a nothosaur, Lariosaurus; and a turtle, Triassochelys. In front are some Triassic fish: left, a shark; middle, a shoal of bony fish.

They were not the only four-legged animals that returned to the sea; several types of reptile also took to the waves. In Triassic rocks we find fossils of an early turtle, called *Triassochelys*. This animal still had teeth, which modern turtles do not possess, for they have a horny beak instead. But otherwise it was much like our turtles.

The most dramatic sea reptiles were the Ichthyosaurs, a name that means "fish reptile." An ichthyosaur was completely fish-shaped: with a streamlined body, fins instead of legs, a long finned tail and a fin on its back. It had a long mouth with many sharp teeth, a good trap for catching the fish it ate.

Most marine reptiles had to come back on land to

ran along on their hind legs. Surprising as it may seem, they were the ancestors of the giant dinosaurs. They probably ate insects, grubs, snails – any small animal they could find.

Already at the end of the Triassic we find the first dinosaurs; for instance, *Plateosaurus*, a large awkward animal that could walk on its hind legs and probably ate plants.

These first dinosaurs were not yet the most important reptiles. The mammal-like reptiles we saw in the Permian were still flourishing. *Tritylodon* is one of the best known; recently some very good fossil skeletons of it were found in Arizona.

It was about the size of a spaniel. The joints of its

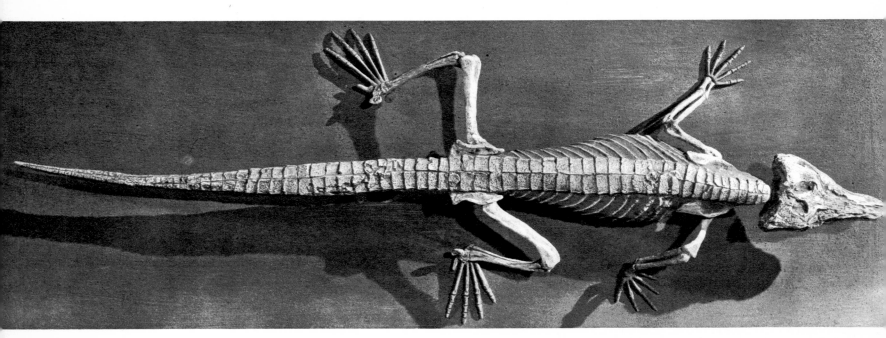

Protosuchus was a small armored Triassic reptile. Though very like a thecodont, it was an early ancestor of the crocodiles of today.

lay their eggs, as the turtles do today. But ichthyosaurs had overcome this problem of sea life too. The eggs were not laid, but hatched inside the mother's body and then the baby ichthyosaur was born. We know that this was so, because we have found a fossil ichthyosaur with fossil baby ichthyosaurs inside it!

Other Triassic sea reptiles were the Nothosaurs. These were not nearly so fishlike as the ichthyosaurs. Their legs were still legs, not fins; but they gradually became more and more sea-going and, in the Jurassic, the Plesiosaurs evolved from them.

On land there were many new types of reptile. There were little Rhynchocephalians – a group with a single survivor, the Tuatara of New Zealand. Small, light-boned Thecodonts, like *Saltoposuchus*,

ribs show that it breathed like a mammal does – in soft, slow, rhythmic gulps. This kind of breathing is associated with warm blood. So perhaps *Tritylodon*, unlike other reptiles, had warm blood even on the coldest night.

If it had warm blood it would have had to have a fur coat to keep it warm. Strangely enough, the parts of its backbone were arranged so that the animal could turn and twist its head and shoulders exactly as it would have to do if it were licking and cleaning fur.

These hairy reptiles are too late in time to be mammal ancestors, for it seems likely that early in the Triassic true mammals were already in the world. But they show us the way in which the mammals evolved from reptiles.

Paracyclotosaurus 10 feet

Cynognathus 8 feet

Plateosaurus 21 feet

Saltoposuchus 4 feet

Triassochelys 3 feet

Episcoposaurus 15 feet

Mastodonsaurus 11 feet

The last great amphibians, like Paracyclotosaurus *and* Mastodonsaurus, *lived in the Triassic; as did the first dinosaurs, like* Plateosaurus. *Other Triassic reptiles pictured here:* Saltoposuchus, *a small thecodont, and* Episcoposaurus, *an armored one;* Cynognathus, *a mammal-like reptile; and* Triassochelys, *a toothed turtle.*

Jurassic—180 million years ago

The 45 million years of the Jurassic were reptile years. The great dinosaurs dominated the lands; the sea reptiles flourished; and two kinds of reptiles even took to the air – the pterosaurs and the birds, which began as reptiles with feathers.

The Jurassic is named after the Jura Mountains on the borders of France and Switzerland. They are made of rocks formed in this period of time.

By the Jurassic, the high mountains which were built at the end of the Paleozoic had been worn down, until most of the lands were low-lying and swampy. The world was mainly warm and damp. There were few, if any, of the hot dry plains, that covered much of the continents during the Permian and Triassic periods.

In the Northern Hemisphere, the one large continent had become two; in the south, Gondwanaland was beginning to split up. Many of the seas were warm and shallow and the rivers carried much material into them. In fact, most of the Jurassic rocks we know were made from sea sediments.

The Jurassic rocks have many tales to tell of a profusion of life. As usual, the sea was crowded, or so it seems, with all kinds of animals and plants. Algae helped make little pellets of lime, that in masses look like fish eggs. These formed rocks called oolites (from the Greek word *oon*, meaning egg).

By the Jurassic, dinosaurs had evolved in many ways. Flesh-eating ones, like Antrodemus (1), fed on the plant-eaters, like Stegosaurus (2) which was protected by its rows of bony plates. In the swamps and lakes lived the huge amphibious dinosaurs, like Apatosaurus (3)· which probably reached a weight of 30 tons or more. Small "birdlike" dinosaurs, such as Ornitholestes (4), moved quickly, running on their strong hind legs. But there were other reptiles as well as dinosaurs in the Jurassic: for instance, early crocodiles (5), and flying reptiles, like Pterodactylus (6) and the long-tailed Rhamphorhynchus (7). There were mammals, also (8 and 9), but they were unimportant compared to the dinosaurs. Among Jurassic plants, the newcomers called cycads (10) were abundant.

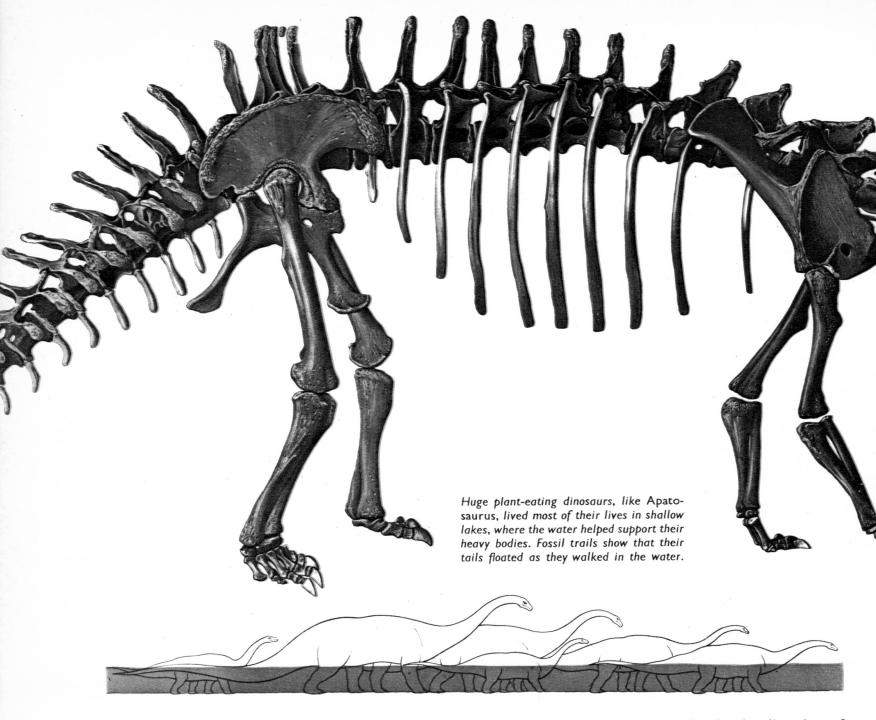

Huge plant-eating dinosaurs, like Apatosaurus, *lived most of their lives in shallow lakes, where the water helped support their heavy bodies. Fossil trails show that their tails floated as they walked in the water.*

There were coral reefs, and also reefs formed by sponges. Moss animals grew everywhere, and many lamp shells lived at this time. But the most common shelled animals were mollusks. Bivalves like *Gryphaea*, an oyster, are found as fossils in many places in England. Ammonites flourished all over the world; again we can use their fossils to identify different rocks. The joint lines of their chambers were fantastically complicated and each kind of ammonite had its own pattern of squiggles (see p. 23) so they are easy to tell apart.

Gastropod mollusks were so abundant that one kind of rock in England, Purbeck marble, is almost entirely made of snail shells.

The bony fish still had thicker scales than modern ones, but were slowly changing in the direction of their present-day counterparts. Sharks and rays, not much different from those living today, were present in the seas in great numbers.

But the monarchs of the Jurassic seas were the sea reptiles. Around the shores, great rowing monsters, up to 30 feet long, paddled their watery way in search of fish and cuttlefish. These were the plesiosaurs – descendants of the nothosaurs of the Triassic. Most of them were small-headed and long-necked, with great flat-bellied bodies. Their legs had become paddles and with these they rowed their heavy bodies through the seas. As an oarsman can turn a boat, they could snap quickly round after their victims by paddling on one side and back-paddling on the other.

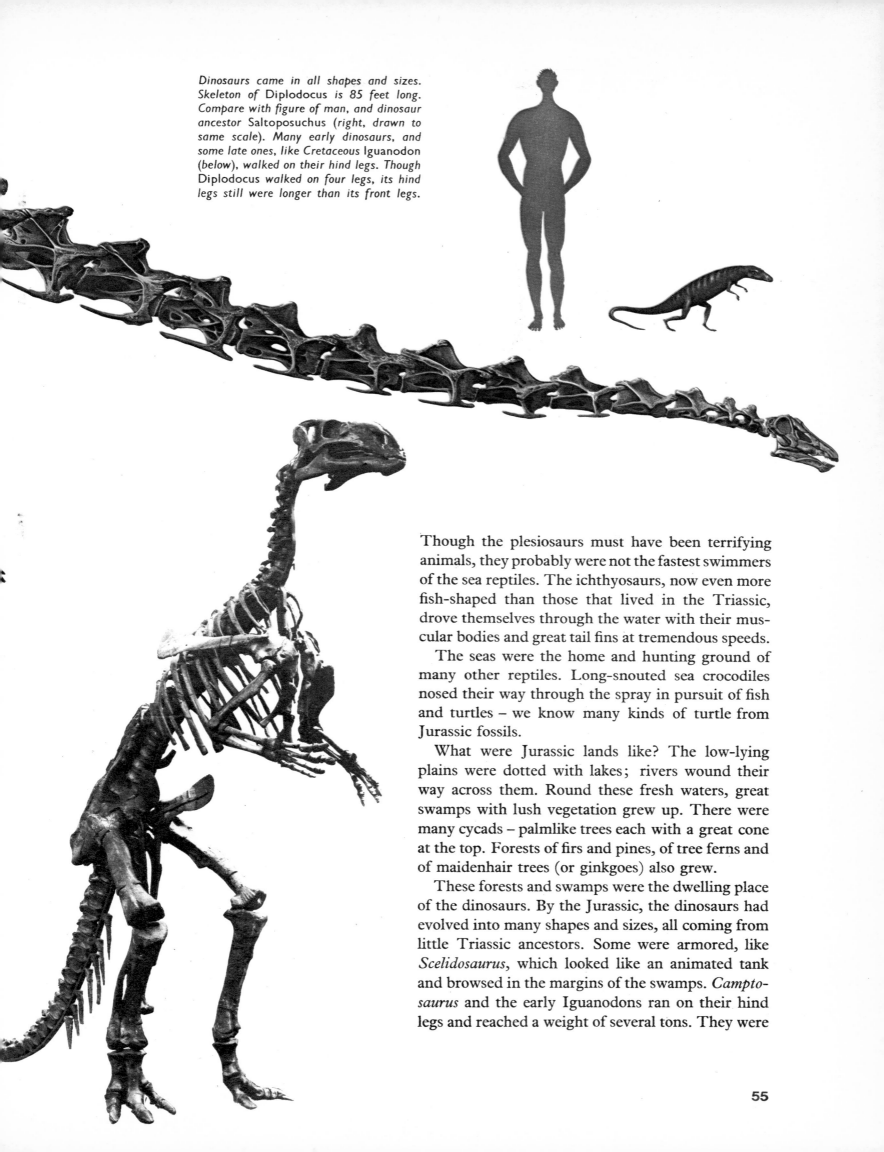

Dinosaurs came in all shapes and sizes. Skeleton of Diplodocus is 85 feet long. Compare with figure of man, and dinosaur ancestor Saltoposuchus (right, drawn to same scale). Many early dinosaurs, and some late ones, like Cretaceous Iguanodon (below), walked on their hind legs. Though Diplodocus walked on four legs, its hind legs still were longer than its front legs.

Though the plesiosaurs must have been terrifying animals, they probably were not the fastest swimmers of the sea reptiles. The ichthyosaurs, now even more fish-shaped than those that lived in the Triassic, drove themselves through the water with their muscular bodies and great tail fins at tremendous speeds.

The seas were the home and hunting ground of many other reptiles. Long-snouted sea crocodiles nosed their way through the spray in pursuit of fish and turtles – we know many kinds of turtle from Jurassic fossils.

What were Jurassic lands like? The low-lying plains were dotted with lakes; rivers wound their way across them. Round these fresh waters, great swamps with lush vegetation grew up. There were many cycads – palmlike trees each with a great cone at the top. Forests of firs and pines, of tree ferns and of maidenhair trees (or ginkgoes) also grew.

These forests and swamps were the dwelling place of the dinosaurs. By the Jurassic, the dinosaurs had evolved into many shapes and sizes, all coming from little Triassic ancestors. Some were armored, like *Scelidosaurus*, which looked like an animated tank and browsed in the margins of the swamps. *Camptosaurus* and the early Iguanodons ran on their hind legs and reached a weight of several tons. They were

Beside a Jurassic lake, a dying Archaeopteryx was caught in fine mud. In a limestone slab (below) we can trace its fossil remains.

Shoulder girdle

Brain case

Toe claw

Impressions of flight feathers

Lower arm bones
Upper arm bone

Lower leg bone
Upper leg bone

Impressions of tail feathers

vegetarians whose shearing teeth could tear leaves from the cycad trees, and whose hands were strong enough to tear the branches down.

The biggest dinosaurs of all lived in the Jurassic, and were also vegetarians. *Diplodocus, Brachiosaurus, Cetiosaurus, Apatosaurus,* were 60 feet or more in length, and over 20 tons in weight. The swamps and estuaries resounded to the splash of these vast amphibious monsters, for they lived most of their lives in water, gathering the soft water plants to keep their huge bodies going. They walked on all four legs, and the nerve center in their hips, that controlled their pillarlike legs, was bigger than the brain in their small heads.

As well as providing lots of easily gathered food, and supporting their huge weight, the swamps helped protect these great, slow-moving hulks from the preying members of their kind. These (relatively) smaller dinosaurs, like *Megalosaurus* and *Antrodemus*, ran swiftly on their hind legs, and could kill with cruel hind claws, and devour with sharp serrated teeth.

Above the battles on the land, and the fierce competition in the sea, were the flying reptiles or Pterosaurs. Awkward in body, with feeble legs, they had long arms and fingers that supported wide sheets of translucent skin. These wings were attached along the body and kept taut by movements of the hind legs. With their wings, the pterosaurs could fly reasonably well – soaring in search of dragonflies, or swooping to snatch a fish from the sea.

The pterosaurs soon had company in the air. In the middle of the Jurassic came the birds. From a limestone quarry at Solnhofen in Germany have come three skeletons of *Archaeopteryx*, the earliest known bird.

This crow-sized creature was a reptile in bird's disguise. It had feathers of a modern kind arranged on a modern plan; but its jaws bore reptile teeth, and its skeleton was arranged like that of a reptile, ending in a long reptile tail with 20 bony vertebrae, nearly all with a pair of overlying feathers.

This tree-glider of feeble flying-power would be unknown to us had not a gale blown these three into the waters of a shallow lake. There they drowned with hardly a struggle, leaving their bones and the imprint of their feathers in the fine sand that soon covered their remains. We do not often find examples of animals like these that are in a "halfway stage" in the evolution of one group into another.

Equally scarce, but equally certain, are the remains of Jurassic mammals. These small furry predecessors of our modern mammalian world have left only jaws and a few fragments of other bones. Careful research has built up, piece by piece, the picture of *Oligokyphus*, near relation of the hairy reptile *Tritylodon* we discussed in the Triassic.

Thus the near mammals, and the true mammals lived side by side. The former died out; the latter lived on – eventually to replace the great reptiles that in Jurassic days overshadowed all.

Ichthyosaurs abounded in Jurassic seas. Fossils found in slate, like this one, sometimes show the fishlike outlines of the animal's body.

In the Cretaceous, the seas covered a lot of the world; the lands (light brown in map above) were much reduced. Australia had finally been cut off from Gondwanaland. Places where chalk was laid down are shown in dark brown. Compare with maps on pages 26 and 42.

Cretaceous—135 million years ago

The name Cretaceous comes from the Latin word for chalk, *creta*. For in this period, great beds of chalk were formed in Europe and North America.

Through the Cretaceous, which was a long period, probably lasting nearly 70 million years, the continents began to move slowly toward their present-day shapes. At the beginning of the Cretaceous, the climate over much of the world was mild, but by the end of the period it was becoming colder.

No new mountains had been built, so the lands were still low-lying, with lush swamps. In America we even get coal beds that were formed in the Cretaceous. Around the coasts, great deltas fanned out into the shallow seas, and in their sediments the bodies of many animals were trapped and preserved.

In the seas, there was a great wealth of all kinds of invertebrates. In shallow warm seas, myriads of tiny shelled animals and plants lived; chalk is almost entirely made up of their shells. A new kind of bivalve mollusk arose that lived fixed by one shell; sometimes these made reefs. Ammonites and belemnites still flourished through most of the Cretaceous but by the end of it had all died out.

The fish of the Cretaceous were fairly modern, and there were many of them; but the reptiles held sway over the seas. Ichthyosaurs were still around, but were no longer so important. The Cretaceous was the heyday of the plesiosaurs. One group, the Elasmosaurs, had enormous necks, up to 20 feet long, that

Plesiosaurs rowed their stumpy bodies through the water with their strong paddles. This Jurassic one was found in Somerset, England.

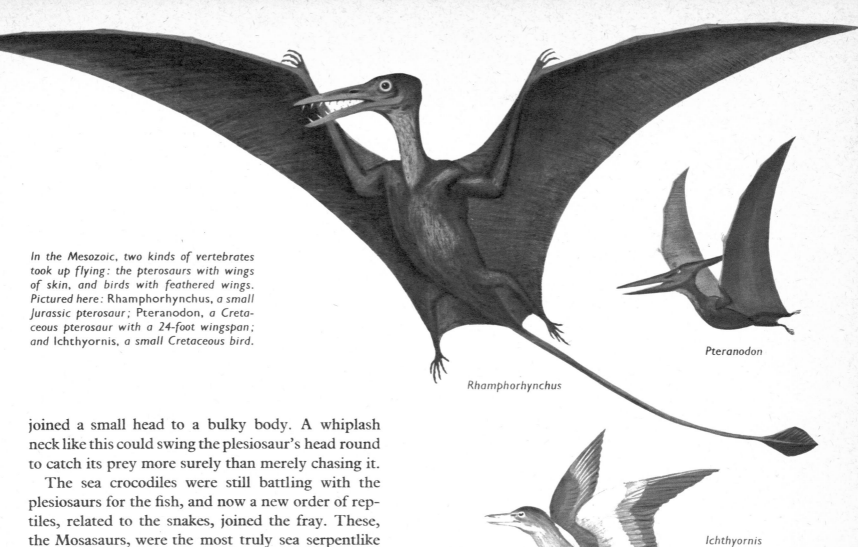

In the Mesozoic, two kinds of vertebrates took up flying: the pterosaurs with wings of skin, and birds with feathered wings. Pictured here: Rhamphorhynchus, *a small Jurassic pterosaur;* Pteranodon, *a Cretaceous pterosaur with a 24-foot wingspan;* and Ichthyornis, *a small Cretaceous bird.*

Pteranodon

Rhamphorhynchus

Ichthyornis

joined a small head to a bulky body. A whiplash neck like this could swing the plesiosaur's head round to catch its prey more surely than merely chasing it.

The sea crocodiles were still battling with the plesiosaurs for the fish, and now a new order of reptiles, related to the snakes, joined the fray. These, the Mosasaurs, were the most truly sea serpentlike animals we know. With loosely hinged jaws that could open to engulf large prey, and with cruel teeth, these swimming monsters sometimes reached 50 feet long. We find their fossils only in late Cretaceous rocks, but their remains are found in many places all over the world.

Over the seas, the pterosaurs soared. Some were small: *Pterodactylus* was only the size of a sparrow; but *Pteranodon* had a span of 27 feet from wing-tip to wing-tip. This giant weighed about 60 pounds; but its bones were hollow, and air-filled. It lived like a reptilian albatross, spending perhaps days away from the cliffs that were its home, soaring over the wave crests and then diving as it saw a fish or small reptile worth its while.

The birds had also developed: we know nearly a dozen Cretaceous successors to *Archaeopteryx;* all but one are sea birds. The small ternlike *Ichthyornis* was a strong flier, with large breast muscles and powerful wings. The large *Hesperornis,* nearly five feet long, had no wings, not even arm bones; it was a swimming bird. These two lived in America, but in England there were swimming birds the size of a pigeon, in Sweden there were ancestral flamingoes, and in France the forefathers of the goose.

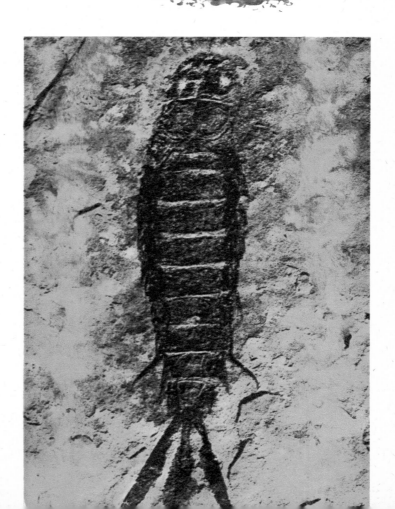

A fossil bristletail from Cretaceous rock. By this period, insects of many kinds flew in the air, while others ran on the ground.

On land the reptiles were still unchallenged. Over Cretaceous lands strode the largest flesh-eater of all time – *Tyrannosaurus*. This terrible animal was 45 feet from nose to tail. Its head was four feet long, and it had many large cruel teeth. It ran on tremendously solid hind legs, but its front legs were tiny and withered-looking; they could not even reach the animal's mouth.

This tyrant chased the duck-billed Hadrosaurs, that also ran on their hind legs. They liked to wade in water and eat the succulent but sandy roots of the horsetails. Hadrosaurs had toes with hoofs, yet they had webs of skin between their toes, and their tail was flattened from side-to-side, both of which suggest that they could swim. Some had great bony crests or "helmets" on the skull that may have held extra air for those that liked to linger over their under-water meals.

The Iguanodons moved ponderously along on their hind legs, through the forests, eating leaves and branches. Most of the other purely land-living dinosaurs of this time were armored. Some bore bony plates all over; others had both spikes and plates for protection.

The greatest of these armored dinosaurs were the Ceratopsians, or horn-faced dinosaurs, like *Triceratops*, which was nearly 30 feet long. Over each eye it had a long pointed horn, over its nose, another; and behind, extending over its neck, was a great protective collar of bone. These horns, no doubt, were defensive, but they could also be used to bend down the little trees whose leaves these animals ate.

The leaves tell a story of changing vegetation. The cycads were less to be seen, but the conifers were still going strong, and new kinds of trees – elms, oaks, maples and others familiar to us – had joined them. Alas, these new trees had no leaves on them for many months of even a Cretaceous year. So plant-eating dinosaurs were beginning to feel the want of the old lush vegetation that used to provide food all the year round.

With the change in climate, as the swamps and lakes drained and the land grew drier, and as the little mammals developed and became more prominent inhabitants of the earth, the dinosaurs began to lose their command. When the white cliffs of Dover were being laid down, the dinosaurs had mostly disappeared, forever.

The Mesozoic, the Middle Age of Life, was over, 70 million years ago.

One of the Cretaceous dinosaurs was the biggest flesh-eater that has ever lived on land – Tyrannosaurus, measuring 45 feet from nose to tail. Also living in the Cretaceous were the duck-billed dinosaurs, like Trachodon (on the left). Struthiomimus (in background) was one of the smaller, birdlike dinosaurs. Palaeoscincus (right) was an armored dinosaur, a plant-eater that walked on all four legs.

Quaternary	Woolly mammoth · Teratornis · Woolly rhinoceros · Giant ground sloth · Man
Pliocene	Mastodon · Glyptodon · Saber-tooth cat · Shovel tusker · Pliohippus
Miocene	Phororhacos · Alticamelus · Dinotherium · Proconsul · Syndyoceras · Merychippus
Oligocene	Fly from amber · Hyaenodon · Archaeotherium · Brontotherium · Baluchitherium · Mesohippus
Eocene	Coryphodon · Uintatherium · Lithornis · Early whale · Ectoconus · Early primate · Eohippus
Cretaceous	Ichthyornis · Trachodon · Tyrannosaurus · Triceratops · Portheus · Iguanodon · Pteranodon · Elasmosaurus
Jurassic	Archaeopteryx · Diplodocus · Rhamphorhynchus · Early mammal · Antrodemus · Stegosaurus
Triassic	Mixosaurus · Triassochelys · Cynognathus · Lariosaurus · Paracyclotosaurus · Bony fish · Saltoposuchus
Permian	Pleuracanthus · Ophiacodon · Seymouria · Palaeoniscus · Eryops · Dimetrodon
Carboniferous	Dolichosoma · Meganeura · Petrolacosaurus · Diplovertebron · Amphicentrum · Mesosaurus · Miobatrachus
Devonian	Lamp shell · Ichthyostega · Cladoselache · Placoderm · Cheirolepis · Eusthenopteron · Cup coral
Silurian	Ostracoderm · Eurypterid · Lamp shell · Cephalopod · Coral colony · Trilobite · Gastropod
Ordovician	Cephalopod · Moss animal colony · Trilobite · Starfish · Lamp shell · Graptolite · Sea lily · Cup coral
Cambrian	Onychophoran · Trilobite · Crustacean · Jellyfish · Echinoderm · Sponge · Worm

Modern mammals evolve, reach their peak at end of Pliocene and start of Quaternary. Many, particularly large ones, then die out.

Some ancient mammals continue; modern mammals begin to take on familiar shapes

[mod]ent mammals reach their [p]eak, then die out. Baltic [am]ber formed, from resin

No dinosaurs. Birds well [re]presented. Invertebrates much like modern ones. Rise of mammals.

Last dinosaurs. Mosasaurs and plesiosaurs in seas. Giant pterosaurs. Birds of several kinds. Mammals still small and [o]bscure. Chalk formed in [m]any shallow warm seas.

Rise of great dinosaurs. Plesiosaurs. First flying [r]eptiles, and birds. Early mammals. Ammonites.

Last great amphibians. First dinosaurs. First [ic]hthyosaurs, early turtles and nothosaurs in seas.

[A]mphibians continue: rep[ti]les becoming important, [p]articularly the fin-backs. First bugs and beetles.

Coal-forming forests: [a]mphibians flourish: some [l]arge; many small. First [r]eptiles at end of period. First winged insects.

[M]any fish: ostracoderms; [pla]coderms; first sharklike [fi]sh; first bony fish. Land invertebrates of several kinds. First land vertebrates: amphibians.

First fossil land plants and animals. First fish (placoderms) at end of [p]eriod. Many coral reefs.

Increase of mollusks, [p]articularly cephalopods. First fossil vertebrates: [o]stracoderms. No fossils of land life.

All main groups of in[v]ertebrates in the seas. [T]rilobites the commonest fossils. No life on land.

Some of the animals mentioned in this book are here shown in their place on the time scale (see p. 25). Animals are pictured only in periods when their group was important: for instance, no reptiles are shown after the Cretaceous, though the group continued after that time, and still survives. But after the Cretaceous, reptiles were less important than birds and mammals.

61

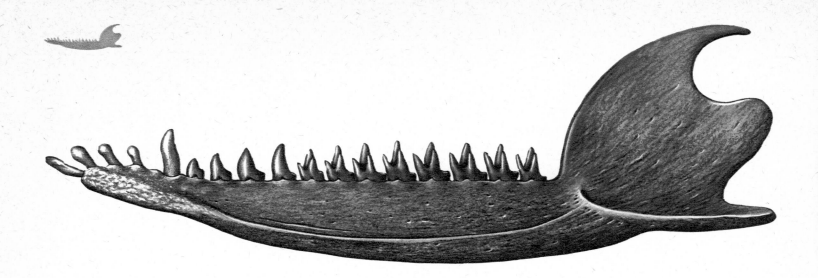

Tiny jawbones, like that of Amblotherium (above, natural size at top left) are almost the only clues we have to the early mammals. But we can guess that they were shrewlike animals, as in this reconstruction of Jurassic Phascolotherium; compare their size with that of the dinosaur eggs.

Mammals Rule the Earth

When the last of the great dinosaurs died, their successors were already living – ready to inherit the earth. The end of the age of reptiles was the beginning of the age of mammals.

Of course there were still reptiles on earth, as there are today, but the time of their dominance was over. We have seen that changes in climate, geography and plants must have made life difficult for the great land reptiles, and that they were, in the end, defeated by these changes. It is more difficult to guess why the great sea reptiles – the ichthyosaurs, plesiosaurs and mosasaurs – gradually faded away and died out while the fish, crocodiles and turtles survived. And in the air, the pterosaurs that had been so successful for millions of years, vanished; yet the birds went from strength to strength.

Whatever the causes of the reptiles' decline, there is no doubt of its importance: it allowed the mammals, small and living in obscurity for 100 million years, to develop. They multiplied in number and in kind on land; some became adapted for life in the sea, and one group (the bats) took up flying, though the birds were the really successful air dwellers. At the start of the Tertiary, almost all the main families of birds we know today were in the world. They have spread enormously, and are now one of the most successful groups of animals.

At the beginning of the Tertiary, the chalk that was formed in the Cretaceous had just been raised and become land. New mountains were building – the Alps, the Rockies, the Himalayas, the Andes: all the high mountains of today.

The climate over most of the world was still warm as the Tertiary began – though cooler than in the Cretaceous. But the world slowly continued to get colder, until at last in the Quaternary Era, most of the Northern Hemisphere lay under great ice sheets.

The mammals were well equipped to withstand this slow lowering of the temperature. They had warm blood and coats of hair to keep them warm. They did not lay eggs that had to be hatched by the warmth of the sun, as the reptiles did. Instead, their young developed – warm, protected and well fed – inside the body of the mother.

What were the mammals like, 70 million years ago? Many were shrewlike, as the Jurassic ancestors of the whole group had been. Among the mammals of this time, the Eocene, we can trace the ancestors of most of the kinds of mammal alive today. There were animals with sharp tearing teeth and claws, forefathers of the modern flesh-eaters. These primitive carnivores must have hunted the first hooved mammals which were plant-eaters with grinding teeth. The first whales were already in the seas – seas that contained fish and invertebrates much like those of today.

London looked like this, 60 million years ago when an open sea met southern England. A swamp formed on a great river delta; most of the kinds of plants that grew in it still grow today, but mainly in tropical lands. In this reconstruction are Sabal palms (1), and the smaller Nipa palms (2), tall swamp cypresses (3), magnolias (4), and broad-leaved trees like oak and walnut. In this swamp lived bulky mammals, like Coryphodon (5), and the smaller Hyraco-therium (6); shrewlike mammals (7) and marsupials (8) dwelt in the undergrowth; and in the sea was an early whale, Zeug-lodon (9). There were many birds: a king-fisher, Halcyornis (10), a vulture, Lith-ornis (11); gannetlike Odontopteryx (12) and the flightless Gastornis (13). Croco-diles (14) and tortoises (15) splashed in the pools. Fossils of these are in London Clay.

In the trees were small nimble animals (primates) first in the line of evolution that leads to monkeys and apes and men. The trees they lived in were very like the ones we know, with flowers, and broad leaves that were shed in winter.

In the study of fossil mammals, geography is important, because we know so many fossils from each continent. Australia separated from the rest of Gondwanaland during the Cretaceous, and most of the mammal groups never got there. Instead, the marsupial mammals, which did, filled all the spaces left by the decline of the reptiles.

Marsupials did well in South America, too. From the Eocene to the Pliocene, this continent was not connected to North America. The mammals that

reached South America evolved on their own, some groups expanding enormously – like the gnawing mammals which are still abundant in South America, the sloth and armadillo group, and several strange groups of grazing mammals.

When South America and North America were joined again, in the Pliocene, waves of invaders spread south, and a few went north. Many of the special South American mammals became extinct: the competition of the more modern North American mammals was too much for them.

North America, Europe, Asia and Africa were all, at least sometimes, connected to each other by land, so animals could move between them.

In the Eocene, we find early members of many

groups and by the Oligocene some of these, particularly the grazing mammals, developed large forms; like the brontotheres, relatives of the rhinoceroses. But by the end of the Oligocene, most had died out.

In the next period, the Miocene, we find more modern mammals, as well as members of groups unknown today. But these, too, had vanished by the end of the Pliocene, the next period and a short one.

In the Pliocene, the modern mammals developed, and in the following period, called the Pleistocene, which began about a million years ago, the peak of modern mammal development was reached. There were many giant forms: huge mammoths and mastodons, ground sloths 18 feet high, enormous bison, beavers seven feet long and even, in Australia, giant marsupials. But for some reason, almost all the giant mammals, and many smaller ones, had gone by the end of the Pleistocene. The mammals of today are only a poor remnant of the great age of mammals.

The fossils of the Tertiary are, as we would expect, both more common and better preserved than those of earlier Eras. Paleontologists have been able to find almost complete series of fossils showing the evolution of some of the modern mammals. Now let us look at one of these – the story of the horse – and at some exciting fossil mammals.

Mammals have taken up many ways of life. Bats fly; horses run; monkeys use their versatile limbs both for swinging and handling objects; tigers spring and whales swim. Below: Baluchitherium, the biggest land mammal, lived 40 million years ago. It stood over 17 feet high.

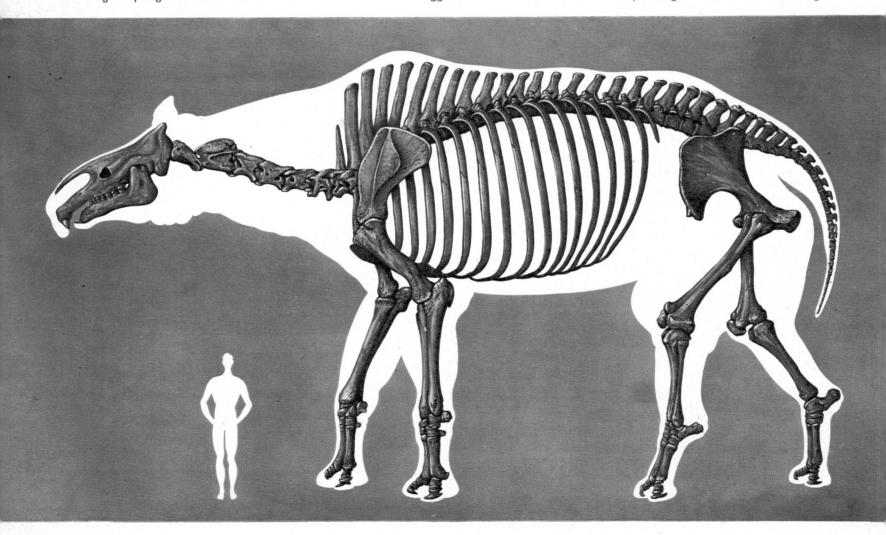

Glyptodon   9 feet long

Amebelodon   25 feet from trunk tip to tail

Brontotherium   8 feet high at shoulder

Syndyoceras   size of small deer

Alticamelus   head 10 feet from ground

Hyaenodon   3½ feet long

Archaeotherium   8 feet long

Reconstructions of some fossil mammals look like caricatures of modern mammals, but because most large animals today are mammals, fossil mammals look more familiar than fossil reptiles. Amebelodon was a shovel-tusker; Archaeotherium was related to pigs; Hyaenodon was a carnivore; Uintatherium was a large Eocene mammal.

Uintatherium   9 feet long

Eohippus *lived in forests where it browsed on leaves, for its short teeth could only grind up soft food.* Eohippus *had four toes on its front feet; three toes on its hind feet.*

Merychippus *was larger than* Eohippus, *and lived in more open country. It had three toes on both front and hind feet, but the central toe was much stronger than the two side toes, which did not touch the ground.*

The modern horse Equus *(left, below) is almost three times the size of* Eohippus *(right). Other differences between them are in teeth, length of leg, and number of toes.*

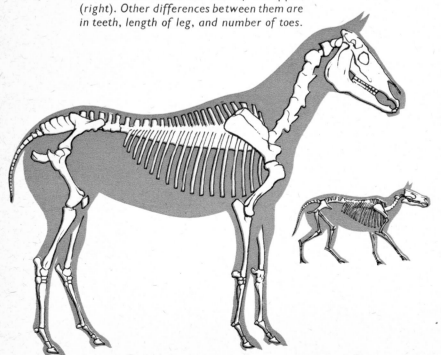

Horses

In the clay that London is built upon are fossil bones of a small animal called *Hyracotherium* ("shrew-beast," see page 64). It is hard to connect this little beast of the bushes with the large modern horse of the plains. Yet *Hyracotherium*, and the very similar *Eohippus* ("dawn horse") of America, were the starting material from which horses came.

Hyracotherium and *Eohippus*, both from the Eocene, were about the size of a fox-terrier; they had browsing teeth, four toes on their front feet and three on their hind feet. In the Oligocene, came *Mesohippus* ("middle horse") – a new type. It was about the size of a sheepdog, and on all feet had three toes touching the ground. *Mesohippus* lived in woods and the clearings in them, munching soft leafy vegetation with its browsing teeth.

Merychippus ("cud-chewing horse") was the next

Pliohippus *lived on open plains, grazing on hard grasses with its long teeth. It had one functional toe on each foot, as Equus has.*

stage in horse evolution. These animals were larger, about three feet six inches tall, with teeth that could grind tougher food than leaves. The grasses were beginning to spread over the world when *Merychippus* was alive, 25 million years ago, and horses were leaving the shelter of the forests for the plains.

From *Merychippus* we can trace a number of different kinds of horses that ranged far and wide

and nearly all of which became extinct before long. The real successor, living in the Pliocene some 10 million years ago, was *Pliohippus* ("more of a horse") which had one main toe on each foot as the modern horse has, though *Pliohippus* had side toes that perhaps showed a little. *Pliohippus* was bigger, with longer legs, than any of its predecessors, and had teeth like a modern horse with which it grazed on the grasses of the open plains that were its home.

From *Pliohippus* came several types of horse: the most interesting was *Equus* – the modern horse. It arose in North America about a million years ago.

At that time, the Pleistocene, North America and Asia were joined by land, so the new swift horse, *Equus*, spread throughout the world. Later, all the horses in America died out. When man came to the Americas there were no horses: the horse had to be introduced by man into the home of its long history.

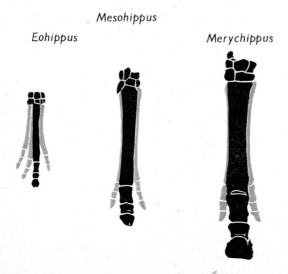

Mesohippus

Eohippus

Merychippus

Equus

Eohippus *had four-toed front feet; Equus uses only one toe on each foot. This evolutionary series shows how other toes (blue) became smaller, while central toe enlarged.*

The fossil ape Proconsul lived in Kenya, 25 million years ago. Modern apes, like the gorilla and gibbon (left), ape-men and men (opposite page) could all have come from animals like Proconsul.

Apes, ape-men and men

Another series of fossils, even more interesting but less complete than those which tell the story of the horse, are those which tell the story of man.

You have probably heard that man is descended from apes. This is true, but the apes that were our ancestors were not like the apes of today. The modern apes are our distant cousins, not our ancestors. They and we have come from the same kind of animal, a kind that lived many millions of years ago.

What was this ape and human ancestor like? Probably like *Proconsul*, which lived in the Miocene, 25 million years ago, in the forests and bushy grasslands of East Africa. *Proconsul* could swing from tree to tree using its arms, or run on all fours on the ground. Its very flexible hands and feet could be used in many ways, and its forward-facing eyes enabled it to judge distances well.

Late in the Miocene, East Africa became drier, and forests remained in only a few places. Perhaps one group of *Proconsul* stayed in the forests and evolved in several ways into the apes of today.

But another group of *Proconsul* perhaps ventured out on to the plains and evolved into a walking animal – man.

We can only guess this, for our next fossil clue comes from Pleistocene deposits of South Africa. In these are fossil bones of animals that are partly ape-like, partly manlike. These ape-men, called Australopithecines, were not very large – about four feet tall. They had small brains, and protruding jaws,

Australopithecines walked upright, like men, but they still had protruding jaws, overhanging brows and small brains, like apes. They used, and perhaps made, simple tools and weapons from stones.

Pithecanthropus had a body very like modern man's, but still had rather apelike brows and jaws. He made tools of many kinds from sticks and stones; and hunted quite large animals with his weapons.

like an ape; but their limbs and backbones show they stood upright.

Because the Australopithecines walked upright, their feet could not do so many things as an ape's foot can. An ape can use its big toe in the way we use our thumb. But walking erect meant that the Australopithecines could use their hands more. They lived in open country and used sticks and stones to kill small animals.

The next chapter in the story of man comes from Java and China. There, 500,000 year old remains of the first men – *Pithecanthropus* – have been found.

These still had rather apelike brows and protruding jaws, but their brains were much bigger than those of the Australopithecines. *Pithecanthropus* not only used tools – he made them, by chipping

bits off one pebble with another to give a sharp edge. These first men knew how to make fire to keep warm, and protect themselves from animals.

There were many other sorts of men living in the Pleistocene. The only ones we know much about are the Neanderthals, who were short – mostly about five feet high – and thick set. They had protruding jaws, and overhanging brows, but they made tools of many kinds from sticks and pebbles, and wrapped themselves in the skins of the animals they killed.

The Neanderthal men all died out, and were replaced by modern man, *Homo sapiens*, who had evolved separately from *Pithecanthropus*. Gradually modern man spread over the whole world. Now he has come to dominate all other living things. The last period of time, the Recent, is the age of man.

Neanderthal man had a more thickset body than Pithecanthropus. He was a hunter, and lived in the last great cold spell of the Ice Ages.

A saber-tooth cat attacks a mastodon trapped in the tar at La Brea. Birds of prey (Teratornis) and a wolf wait their turn; a stork runs past.

The tar pits of Rancho La Brea

In a small park (Hancock Park) in the great city of Los Angeles, California, there is a small railed-off lake. It looks like an ordinary lake, but it is not – it is a pool of tar. There are several of these pools in that locality, which has long been known as Rancho La Brea.

The tar seeps up through rock and sand and accumulates in pools, which are liquid in the middle but more solid round the edges. Dust collects on these solid edges, and when it rains, water lies for a time on the tarry dust.

These pools are now guarded, but about 140,000 years ago, they lay in the middle of a plain. When it rained, animals smelt the water lying on the pools from far off and galloped up to drink their fill. As they stepped onto the pool edge, they became stuck in the tar, and the more they struggled the worse their position became. Their cries of distress brought the flesh-eaters hurrying – wild cats, wolves

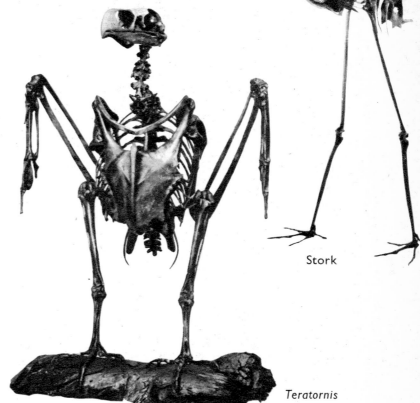

and birds of prey. The flesh-eaters stepped in to begin their feast, only to become bogged themselves.

Slowly the trapped animals sank deeper into the tar, which dissolved away their flesh, claws and beaks, but preserved every bone. Again and again this happened, over hundreds of years, until the pools hid many bones.

About 55 years ago, fossil hunters discovered that these pools contained bones. Scientists came to investigate, and collected the remains of many mammals and birds. Some of these were close relatives of the animals living in California today; but some no longer live in North America; and others are extinct.

There were great mammoths and mastodons, huge ground sloths, camels, bison and horses. There were peccaries and tapirs, wolves, coyotes and foxes. Also many great cats, such as *Smilodon*, the great saber-tooth "tiger" and *Panthera atrox*, a lionlike animal. There were as well some smaller animals; but on the whole it was the big mammals and flesh-eaters that were trapped by the tar. The birds that were caught included storks, geese, cranes, pigeons, crows, larks, owls and many vultures.

The bones of these animals are so well preserved that we can find on them the marks of the diseases and injuries that the animals suffered.

Another very similar tar trap has recently been discovered in Peru, and from it there have already come remains of animals that are new to scientists.

Stork

Teratornis

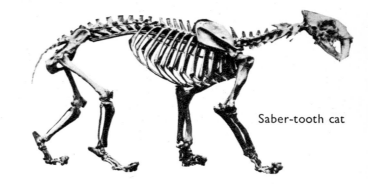

Saber-tooth cat

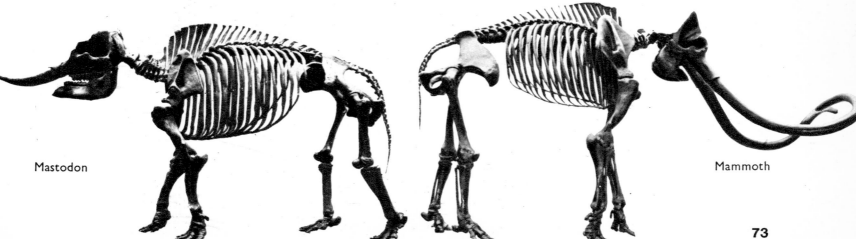

Mastodon

Mammoth

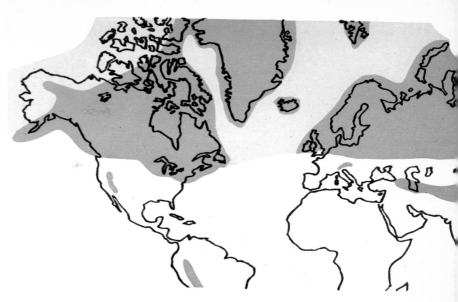

During the Ice Ages, men depended on animals like the woolly rhinoceros for both food and clothes. Map shows how far south the ice spread: dark blue shows ice sheets; light blue, pack ice on the sea.

The great Ice Age

There have been many ice ages, some in lands that are very warm today. But the great Ice Age, the one we know most about, began about 600,000 years ago, in the middle of the Pleistocene period.

It was not continuously cold and icy. There were four glacial times, separated by long, warm times. When the Ice Age began, the temperature grew lower. More snow fell; this packed down into ice, and eventually formed sheets of ice and glaciers. These spread down from the Arctic, across Northern Europe and America. As the ice pushed its vast weight over the land, it scratched rocks and gouged out valleys.

Before this cold and inhospitable bulldozer, most plants and animals retreated. A few became able to endure all but the worst of the icy blasts. The great mammoth, covered in long hair, moved over the frozen soil, picking at tough grasses and lichens. The woolly rhinoceros roamed the bleak countryside, as did herds of reindeer; while in the shelter of the caves, dwelt the great cave bear.

Then, on an average about 60,000 years later, the climate got warmer. The ice retreated, leaving its load of pebbles, rock and sand to show where it had once been. Many plants soon spread over the land that had been under ice, and slowly and surely the animals followed. Lions ranged up into the north of England, and hippopotamuses played in the waters of the Thames, where London now is.

It is now over 20,000 years since the ice left England and southern Scandinavia: too soon to tell if it will come back again. Maybe in another 40,000 years our descendants will know.

Conrad Gesner, a famous naturalist of the 16th century, included these, some of the earliest drawings of fossils, in his books.

Fossil Hunting

One day, 30,000 years ago, a woman found some strangely-shaped stones. She had never seen any like them before, and as they were pretty and rare, she strung them into a necklace. Archaeologists found this necklace, made of fossil sea shells, in a grave with her bones. This nameless woman was one of the first fossil collectors.

As we saw on page 17, fossils have been known for a long time. Greek and medieval scholars argued about fossils: what they were and how they were formed. But they did not go and look for fossils.

In the 17th and 18th centuries, a few people began to collect fossils as curiosities; and some of the famous specimens in museums come from these collections. But it was not until the beginning of the 19th century that fossil hunting began in earnest.

In France, the Abbé Giraud Soulavie published books showing that certain layers of rock contained characteristic fossils. The great Frenchman, Baron Cuvier, was quick to see how important this was, and began to collect fossils and study them, particularly fossils of animals with backbones. From his studies, Cuvier was able to draw accurate reconstructions of a few prehistoric animals; for instance, he drew the reconstruction of an early mammal called *Palaeotherium* shown on page 18.

Industry in England was growing fast at this time, for the Industrial Revolution was well under way. New roads, railroads and especially canals meant much work for surveyors and engineers. William Smith was a surveyor who worked on making canals. He noticed that the layers of rock often contained fossils, some of which were found only in one particular layer. A type of rock could be traced with

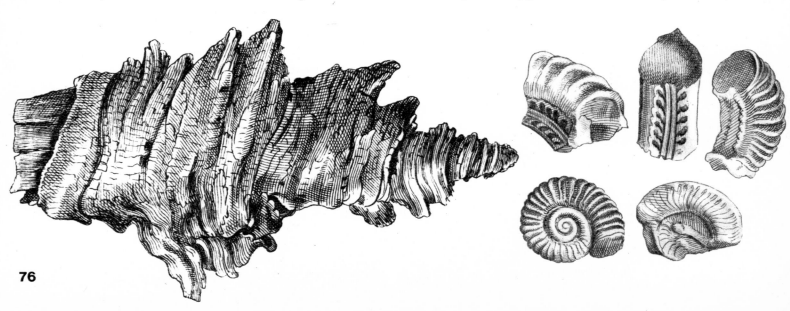

By the 17th century, people had begun to recognize fossil plants as well as animals. The drawings opposite are from a book, published in 1637, by the Italian Stelluti which was almost entirely about plant fossils. Digging mines and canals, like the Manchester Ship Canal (above), and making roads and railroads, revealed more fossils. Coal, being itself the remains of swamp forests, was also a good source, of plant fossils in particular; many leaf imprints, like those shown at right, came from it.

The Frenchman, Baron Cuvier, was a pioneer in the study of rocks and fossils, particularly the fossils of animals with backbones.

William Smith (above) studied fossils to identify rock layers. Mary Anning (left) discovered the first ichthyosaur and plesiosaur. Gideon Mantell (below) first found bones of Iguanodon.

certainty by the kind of fossil it contained. So Smith made extensive collections of fossils for this purpose, to help him prepare his geological map of England, which was published in 1815.

Living at the same time as Smith, in the little seaside town of Lyme Regis in Dorset, England, was a girl called Mary Anning. She was the daughter of a carpenter who occasionally found fossils and sold them to collectors to eke out his meager living. Mr. Anning died at a comparatively early age, and Mary carried on the work she had learned from him.

The study of geology and of fossils was growing in popularity, and Mary Anning was able to sell fossils to University professors and to gentlemen who collected fossils as a hobby. Mary was the first person to find a fossil ichthyosaur; and she found it when she was only 12 years old. Ten years later she found the first plesiosaur, and when she was 40, she found a pterodactyl, the first discovered in England.

Mary Anning soon realized many of the difficulties of fossil collecting. Fossils that are easy to see are often hard to get out of the rock and carry away. She marked her fossil in the cliff or on the beach by leaving her little dog, Tray, sitting by it, and then she fetched workmen who came with hammers, crowbars and picks to dig out the fossil.

Another famous collector of the mid-19th century was a country doctor who lived at Solnhofen, in Germany, an area where the rocks are of fine limestone. There were many quarries there, for this was a stone used in lithography, and the quarrymen often found fossils. Dr. Häberlein was so interested in fossils that he accepted them as fees from the quarrymen he attended. In this way he collected hundreds of them, including that of the early bird *Archaeopteryx* (see p. 56). The British Museum bought most of his first collection, and his *Archaeopteryx* fossil can be seen there.

Another man who combined being a doctor with collecting fossils was Gideon Mantell, who lived in Sussex, England. In 1822, he discovered the bones of an *Iguanodon*, the first fossil dinosaur bones ever found, though dinosaur footprints had been seen

Sir Richard Owen (far left) was one of the great early paleontologists; but he believed that all the fossils he studied had been specially created, each in its own form. Charles Darwin (left) first suggested a way in which animal types could change, by natural selection, thus showing that fossils could be the ancestors of modern animals.

Two Americans, Othniel Charles Marsh (left) and Edward Drinker Cope (right), will always be famous for their work on dinosaurs.

western America sometimes found fossils – a different sort of treasure from the one they were seeking.

Two men dominated the study of fossils in America at the end of the 19th century: Edward Drinker Cope (1840–1897) worked at Philadelphia; his rival, Othniel Charles Marsh (1831–1899), was professor of paleontology at Yale University.

These two men had only to hear a hint of a fossil, and they had parties of fossil hunters on the way to collect the prize, each trying to be the first to bring it back. Many of the great dinosaurs from Wyoming and Colorado, were the fruits of these expeditions.

By the end of the 19th century, fossil hunting had become a large-scale activity. No longer was it a case of collections made, as a hobby, by one man. Expeditions of 20 or 30 or more men set out on the trail of the past. Many of these expeditions were organized and financed by museums.

The American Museum of Natural History even sent expeditions to Mongolia; between 1921 and 1930, these expeditions, led by Roy Chapman Andrews, explored the Gobi Desert and found many fossils. One of the most exciting discoveries they made were of nests of dinosaur eggs. Scientists knew that dinosaurs most probably laid eggs, but no one had found them in such good condition before.

To list all the fossil hunters – even just the great ones – and the places where they collected, would take a whole book, but wherever fossils were found and whoever found them, the same problems

earlier. Mantell's *Iguanodon* was not described until 1825, and in the previous year, Professor Buckland of Oxford University, described *Megalosaurus* – the first named dinosaur in scientific records.

Describing and studying fossils once they have been found is very important. This was Sir Richard Owen's speciality, and it was Owen who first invented the name Dinosauria for a group of reptiles.

By the mid-19th century, all over Europe there were fossil hunters, or paleontologists, hard at work. But the rich hunting grounds of western North America were still untouched. As the pioneers pushed westward, they occasionally found fossils. And the men who followed the gold rushes to the mountains of

Between 1921 and 1930, the American Museum of Natural History sent expeditions to Inner Mongolia to explore the Gobi Desert, and to look for fossils. One of the most exciting discoveries they made were nests of well-preserved eggs of a small dinosaur called Protoceratops. Roy Chapman Andrews (seated at the right) led these expeditions.

Who finds fossils? Wherever men dig in the ground – mining, making roads, digging tunnels, building houses – they may find fossils. But paleontologists no longer rely on chance-found fossils alone. Now expeditions are sent out to look for fossils in specially selected places.

existed: how to get the fossils safely out of the ground, how to get them home, and how to preserve and show them in museums.

Expeditions do not just *find* fossils – it is not as easy as that. The successful party is the one that has been carefully planned.

The early fossil hunters looked for fossils in places where one had been found by chance. Some fossils turned up in mines, or as roads or railroad cuttings were made or canals were dug. Others were found by people as they walked on beaches, or by rivers, or in mountains. Fossil collectors assumed that where there was one fossil there might well be more. There were no geological maps to help them then.

Now we can search for fossils more scientifically, by examining a geological map to find where fossils

Discovered in Kansas, this is a particularly interesting fossil of a giant fish, called Portheus; inside it is the fossil of its last meal, a fish called Gillicus. George F. Sternberg, finder of this fossil (kneeling at left), points to the head of Gillicus. Fossil hunters rarely encounter so large a fossil all in one slab of rock like this.

are likely to be. Let us suppose we want to find dinosaur bones. We know that dinosaurs were most plentiful in the late Jurassic and Cretaceous. We look on the map and find outcrops, that is the coming to the surface, of rocks of this age. Then we find an area where it is clear that the rocks have been much eroded: places like badlands and river gorges.

Having selected a suitable place, the fossil-hunting expedition sets off. The expedition must include men who know about dinosaurs, and others who know about bones – how to excavate and repair them – and who can pack up the bones for their long journey back to the university or museum.

The men will take the implements of their trade: field glasses, cameras, notebooks, maps; then crowbars, picks, shovels, hammers, chisels, and all the shellac, plastics, plaster and so on that will be needed to repair and preserve the fossil bones.

When the expedition reaches its selected site, and has made camp and unpacked, the prospecting members search for scattered bones. If they find quite a few bones at the foot of a slope, they search further up the hill where they may find a layer of bones that is gradually being uncovered by erosion, so that as each bone is freed from the surrounding earth, it falls out and rolls down the slope.

If they find a fossil skeleton still in the rock, the paleontologists start work with picks and shovels, using these tools with great care so that they do not damage the fossil. Slowly the rock is removed from the upper part of the bones. The matrix (the rock sticking to the bones) is carefully taken off as much of the skeleton as possible, with hammer, chisel and wire brush, until the surface is fairly clear.

Before he removes any bones, the fossil hunter numbers them all, and draws a chart of how they lie in the rock and takes photographs of them. This is done, because when the skeleton reaches the laboratory the original position of the bones and the way they were fitted together may have been disturbed.

How is a fossil skeleton prepared for its hazardous journey back to the laboratory? If it is a large one – a big dinosaur, for instance – each bone may have to be removed separately. If it is of a more reasonable size, the fossil hunter will try to transport it in one piece.

The first job is to repair any cracks and breaks in the surface of the bones with shellac. A small bone, or a very small skeleton, can be prized out of the ground with a little rock or earth still sticking to it.

The fossil hunter covers it with thin wet paper and puts plaster over the paper. This protects the fossil in a more or less solid envelope, and the plaster does not stick to the bone because the paper lies between.

Larger bones need more treatment. The fossil hunter removes as much rock as possible from the upper surface, puts wet paper over it, plasters it, covers it over with strips of coarse canvas (burlap) soaked in more plaster, and then plasters strips of

1

2

3

4

5

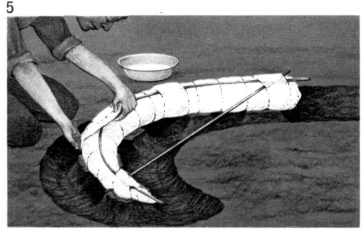

6

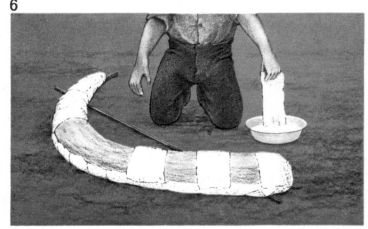

Finding a fossil is only the first step. The paleontologist still has to get it out of the earth where it lies hidden. This may be a tricky business, for fossil bones are often fragile. To begin with, the paleontologist brushes the earth off the fossil, and carefully removes the ground round it (2). Then he paints the fossil (a

mammoth tusk in these diagrams) with shellac to preserve it (3). Next, he covers the exposed side with paper, coats it with plaster (4), reinforces it with metal rods and tunnels through the earth still supporting it (5), so he can more easily lift it. Finally, he turns the fossil over, and plasters and reinforces the other side (6).

wood, or metal rods, over this mass as splints. When he is quite sure that the upper surface is well protected and supported, the fossil hunter removes the rock or earth under the bone. He carefully turns the bone over and repeats the cleaning, repairing, plastering and supporting process on its underside.

The fossil skeleton or bone has now become a large heavy plastered cocoon. The next stage is to get it into a wooden crate. The fossil may have been found halfway up a mountainside, or at the bottom of a steep-sided gorge, and it is often a difficult task to get it away. Large bones may have to be lifted with a block and tackle on a tripod. But with much labor and effort, the prize will eventually be placed in its crate, cushioned on wood wool, or some other soft material, so that it will not be damaged. The crate is numbered and the fossil hunter carefully notes what is in it, where it was found and any other information about it. At last, the fossil is ready to begin its journey back, by truck and railroad.

With a large skeleton, this plastering, lifting and despatching has to be repeated many times; and several skeletons may be found in one season of fossil hunting; so the collector may have to work for many hours a day for months to get them all out; and the more success the expedition has in finding fossils, the harder will he have to work.

When the fossil reaches the museum, the careful work of the fossil hunter in the field then has to be literally undone. The plaster is soaked off, the

On a dry, eroded hillside, paleontologists plaster a fossil bone.

splints are removed, the paper comes away – and there is the bone as it was in the field.

The laboratory workers in the museum now start the fine work of cleaning the fossil. They may remove the last bits of earth and rock with instruments like those used by a dentist. Small pieces are stuck on, cracks are mended, and missing parts may be restored and inserted in plaster or a plastic.

If the fossil bone is large, the cleaning process must be done in parts, for if all the plaster were removed at once, the bone might break under its own weight. So the scientist cleans one side first, and then turns the fossil over onto a bed of fine sand and cleans the underside.

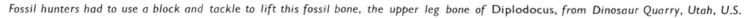

Fossil hunters had to use a block and tackle to lift this fossil bone, the upper leg bone of Diplodocus, *from Dinosaur Quarry, Utah, U.S.*

When the museum has collected a number of preserved and cleaned fossils, what does it do with them? They are studied by experts, named if new to science, catalogued in the museum collection, and then stored. If the specimen is particularly interesting, or very well preserved, it may be exhibited in the galleries of the museum. All this may take much time, especially when the fossil is a new type of animal, and its description and name have to be published in a scientific journal.

Mounting a skeleton to show in the galleries of the museum is a difficult task, too. Experts study the bones to see how they fitted together and where the animal's muscles must have been when it was alive. Thus they discover in what position the skeleton should be mounted. The charts and photographs taken when the skeleton was still in the rock are sometimes helpful at this point. All the bones are laid out on a board, or on the floor if it is a large skeleton, and are carefully fitted together Then special iron supports must be made to hold the

In the museum laboratory, skilled men working with fine instruments clean the last fragments of earth and rock from the fossil.

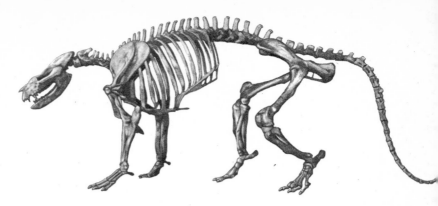

A mounted skeleton gives a good idea of what an animal was like; but a reconstruction gives us a better one. From the bones, a paleontologist can work out what muscles the animal had, and where they were. With this information a skilled artist can draw, or mold, the form of the animal, and from knowledge of the type of country in which it lived, can make a good guess of the animal's coloring, and thus put the finishing touches to the reconstruction.

skeleton in its natural position – to do the work the animal's muscles did when it was alive.

Not all specimens require such time-consuming work. Invertebrates, which are the fossils most often found, are much less difficult to collect and exhibit, because they are smaller, and usually all in one piece, not separated into different parts. But they, too, may require much investigation and delicate skills if we are to understand them scientifically. Sometimes the

fossil is ground away, bit by bit. At each stage the internal structure is studied and photographed, so that at the end, though it has been destroyed, there is a complete series of photographs of the fossil.

Sometimes a paleontologist will put clay and soft deposits in water, where they will break up. He can then study under a microscope the fragments of fossils, and the fossils of tiny animals the clay contains. In some cases the scientist uses ultraviolet

The final adjustments are made to a skeleton mounted on its iron supports in the exhibition hall of the Chicago Natural History Museum.

light to help him distinguish clearly between bone and material in a slab of rock that looks like bone.

Many special skills are needed, if we are to understand the animals of the past. Behind the exhibition rooms of a museum, with their beautifully mounted fossils, there is a hive of activity. Many scientists and technicians are hard at work, discovering more about prehistoric animals and their life.

Now that you have read this book, you may want to collect fossils for yourself. Where will you go?

The easiest places to find fossils are on beaches, below cliffs, such as the cliffs of Dorset, in England. Good places are where rivers and rain have eroded away the rocks, leaving gorges and cliffs, such as the Grand Canyon of Arizona, or the Badlands of South Dakota, in the United States; or the Cheddar or Avon gorges in England. In such places, a good deal of the work of finding fossils may have been done

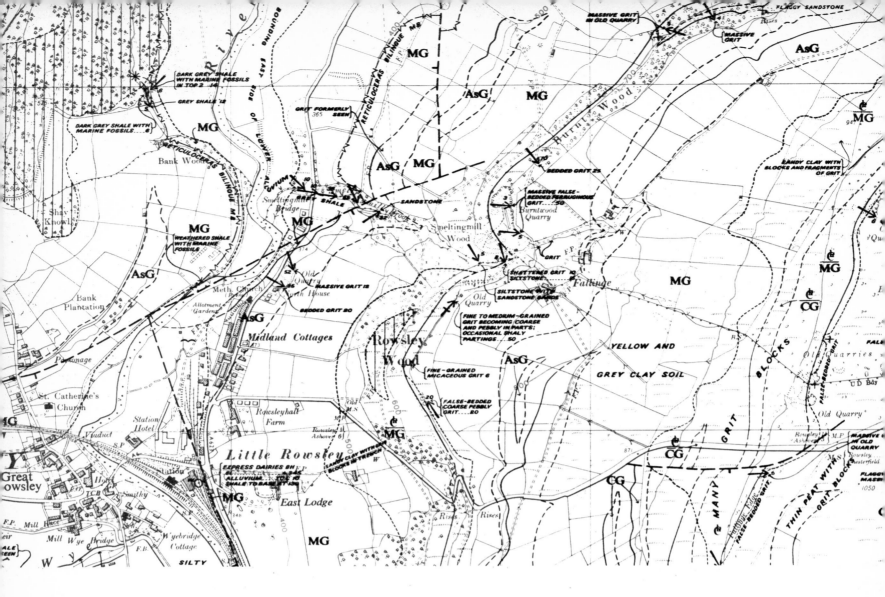

at some time by the sea, river or rain: fossils may be lying on the beach or sticking partly out of the cliff.

Quarries and clay pits, railroad cuttings, road sections, and river banks are other good places to look for fossils, if they cut into the right sort of rocks. If you can find a geological map of the area where you live, study it carefully. It will tell you what sort of rocks lie under the soil, and where there are quarries and so on. Before you hunt for fossils in a quarry or on someone else's land, remember to ask the owner's permission. He may be able to tell you where is the best place to look, and warn you of dangers – for the crumbling cliffs that are the best fossil-hunting grounds can also be dangerous places.

What equipment will you need? A notebook is essential, for a fossil is of little use if you have forgotten where it came from. It is a good idea to photograph the fossils you find before you dig them out of the rock. Getting fossils out of soft rock is fairly easy, and a penknife is a useful tool; but if you find a fossil in a harder rock, a geological hammer is a good implement to have. It has a pointed end, which you can use to prize the fossil out. You will

When you go fossil hunting, study a geological map of the area, like the one above, which is part of a large-scale geological map (2½ inches to the mile) of Derbyshire, England. It shows what the surface rocks are, and in some places, the kind of fossils in them. The special symbol for a fossil locality is shown below; you can also find it on the map, in the top left-hand corner, just west of the river. The conventional signs for five other places where you might find fossils (such as quarries) are also shown below. These are used on ordnance survey as well as geological maps.

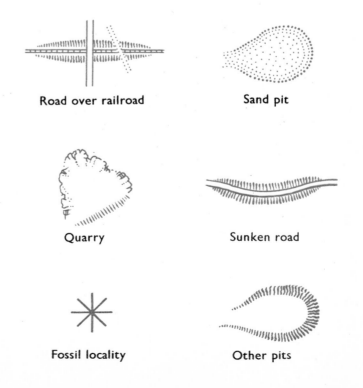

Road over railroad

Sand pit

Quarry

Sunken road

Fossil locality

Other pits

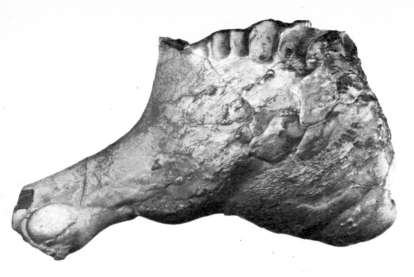

also need: labels; tissue wrapping paper; a hand lens; cloth bags to hold the wrapped fossils; and a rucksack.

When you get your fossil home, clean the earth from it carefully – an old toothbrush is a good tool to use. Then study your find and see if you can identify it.

To be a good fossil collector you must get to know fossils: what they look like and what sort of rock they come from. There are many ways to do this. Study the photographs in this book, and go to a museum and browse in the fossil galleries. Not all museums will let you touch or handle fossils, but do so if you can. Some clays and slates have very typical smells, if you first breathe on them and then sniff; and some rocks have a special taste, so try giving them a lick!

The fossils you are most likely to find are the remains of sea animals, particularly those with shells: ammonites, or parts of ammonites, sea urchins, whelklike shells and so on. Or you may find fossil teeth, particularly sharks' teeth – and if you are very lucky, a bone. Do not be misled by pieces of rock that are shaped like a part of an animal; you will not find a fossil head with eyes and ears like those of a statue, though you may find a piece of rock that is shaped like a head.

Learning about fossils takes time, but if you keep on you will soon be able to recognize the common ones found in your district. If you cannot identify a fossil, take it to your local museum where someone

When you first start fossil hunting, you may occasionally be misled by stones that are shaped like parts of animals, but are not fossils. The stone shown on the left above may look rather like a jawbone with teeth, but if you compare it with the real fossil jawbone and teeth on the right, you will see the difference between the two.

These are some of the types of fossil you might find: lamp shells or their imprints; heart urchins or sea urchins, particularly in chalk; mollusk shells, those of whelklike gastropods for instance; or parts of sea lilies. As well as these fossil invertebrates, you might find fossil teeth or perhaps bones.

Gastropod shell

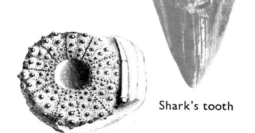

Sea urchin

Shark's tooth

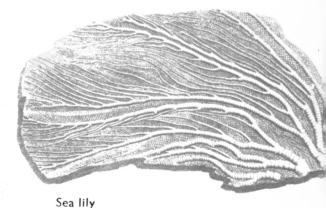

Sea lily

Lamp shells

Heart urchin

This mammoth is mounted in a Leningrad Museum in the position in which it died, trapped in frozen tundra in what is now Siberia.

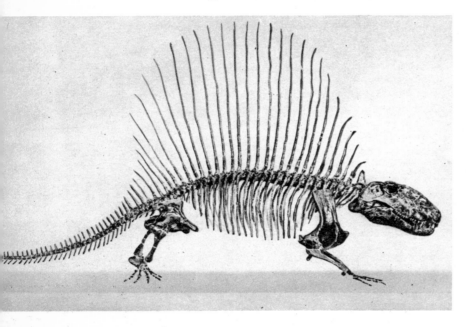

Mounted skeleton of Dimetrodon (above) shows the long spines that supported its "sail" (reconstruction on p. 47). Below: Iguanodons whose mass grave was found near Brussels, where this display is.

may be able to help you and tell you more about it.

Museums are fascinating places, and the more you know, the more fascinating they become. When you go to a museum, read the labels on the fossils carefully. They have been written by experts to help you understand the exhibit, and you can learn a lot from them.

You may wonder about the names of fossil animals. Why do they have such complicated names? Living animals have these long, Latin or Greek names, too, but in ordinary conversation we use their ordinary names: for instance, the Latin, scientific name of the horse is *Equus caballus*. Latin or Greek names are used in scientific works because they are international and cannot be misunderstood as the ordinary names might be.

How do animals get these scientific names? Whoever finds an animal new to science has the privilege of naming it, according to the rules. The scientist may give his new animal a name that describes it in some way – *Tyrannosaurus* means "tyrant lizard," and that 45-foot monster must have been a tyrant indeed – or a name that tells where he found the animal, or that commemorates some famous scientist. The scientific names are in Latin or Greek because when scientists first began to name animals according to a definite system, in the 18th century, Latin was the language all scientists wrote, and the Greek vocabulary gave them a store of further words.

We have to call fossils by their scientific names all the time, because most of them have no ordinary names – though a few of the better known and larger animals have: for instance, the animal called *Megatherium* is also called the giant ground sloth.

When you go to a museum, you will be attracted first by the large skeletons, like the ones in the pictures on these pages. But do not ignore the smaller fossils. They can be just as interesting if you try to imagine what they were like when they were alive: where they lived, and what they ate.

If elephants were unknown, and suddenly someone found one, but knew nothing of where it lived, it would seem a fantastic and impossible animal. But an elephant living peacefully in its home on the plains of Africa is a part of our world. A giant dinosaur at first thought is an extraordinary and weird object. But imagined in its own prehistoric world of 150 million years ago, surrounded by the other animals and plants that lived with it, a dinosaur is no fantasy.

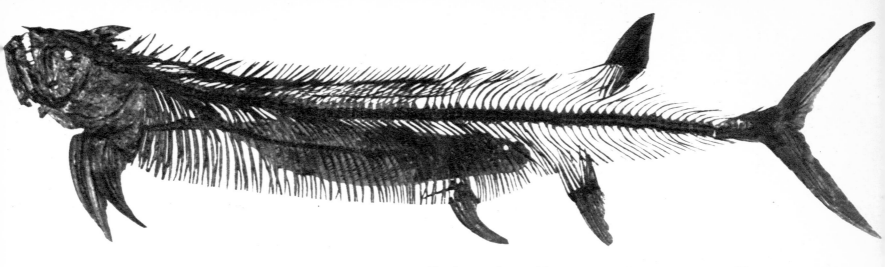

The famous fossil of Portheus, which is shown on page 80 in its original slab of rock before it was taken from the ground, looks like this now that it is displayed in the Fort Hays Kansas State College Museum. You can clearly see the smaller fish, Gillicus, inside the body of Portheus, lying where its stomach must have been.

In many of the great museums of the world, you can see beautifully mounted skeletons of the large dinosaurs, like this one of Apatosaurus (below) which is in the American Museum of Natural History.

Fossil finds

Fossils have been found over the whole world, from Arctic to Antarctic, in almost all sedimentary rocks that fossil hunters have explored. This map shows where some fossil vertebrates were discovered. Where there are no finds marked probably either the land is covered by igneous rock in that region, or no fossil hunters have explored there. Some fossils have been found in more than one place, and in certain cases, the map has several finds for one animal; but others shown as single finds have been found in several places. These, we must emphasize, are only a few of many fossil finds: in Colorado, Wyoming and Montana, for instance, paleontologists have discovered hundreds of fossil vertebrates. In general, fossils on the map are those in this book, or their close relatives

1 JAYMOYTIUS
2 OSTRACODERMS
3 PLACODERMS
4 CLADOSELACHE
5 PLEURACANTHUS
6 EUSTHENOPTERON
7 PORTHEUS
8 ICHTHYOSTEGA
9 ELPISTOSTEGE, another Devonian
    amphibian
10 OPHIDERPETON
11 MIOBATRACHUS
12 ERYOPS
13 MASTODONSAURUS
14 PARACYCLOTOSAURUS
15 PROTOBATRACHUS, an early
    ancestor of the frogs
16 PALAEOBATRACHUS, a fossil frog
17 MESOSAURUS
18 PAREIASAURUS
19 MIXOSAURUS
20 JURASSIC ICHTHYOSAUR
21 LARIOSAURUS
22 PLESIOSAURUS
23 A PLESIOSAUR
24 KRONOSAURUS, a short-necked
    Cretaceous plesiosaur
25 ELASMOSAURUS, a long-necked
    Cretaceous plesiosaur
26 OPHIACODON
27 DIMETRODON
28 DICYNODON, a plant-eating
    mammal-like reptile
29 LYSTROSAURUS, a mammal-like
    reptile that lived partly in water
30 CYNOGNATHUS
31 INOSTRANCEVIA, a mammal-like
    reptile
32 EARLY CROCODILES
33 SALTOPOSUCHUS
34 PLATEOSAURUS
35 EARLY DINOSAURS, like
    Plateosaurus
36 STRUTHIOMIMUS
37 AGROSAURUS, a birdlike dinosaur
38 JUBBULPURIA, a birdlike dinosaur
39 APATOSAURUS
40 BRACHIOSAURUS, a giant
    amphibious dinosaur
41 RHOETOSAURUS, a giant
    amphibious dinosaur
42 CETIOSAURUS, a giant
    amphibious dinosaur
43 TITANOSAURUS, a giant
    amphibious dinosaur, very
    like Diplodocus
44 HELOPUS, a giant amphibious
    dinosaur
45 IGUANODON
46 CARCHARODONTOSAURUS, a
    close relative of the carnivorous
    dinosaur Antrodemus
47 TYRANNOSAURUS
48 PROTOCERATOPS, and its eggs
49 TRICERATOPS
50 STEGOSAURUS

51 PALAEOSCINCUS
52 RHAMPHORHYNCHUS
53 PTERODACTYLUS
54 PTERANODON
55 ARCHAEOPTERYX
56 ICHTHYORNIS
57 PHORORHACOS, a large flightless bird
58 GIANT MOA, a large flightless
    bird, only extinct in last 500 years
59 AMBLOTHERIUM, a Jurassic mammal
60 PALAEOTHERIUM
61 HYAENODON
62 ZEUGLODON
63 CORYPHODON
64 BALUCHITHERIUM
65 BRONTOTHERIUM
66 ALTICAMELUS
67 CAMELOPS, a llamalike camel
68 CAMELUS, modern camel
69 GLYPTODON
70 MEGATHERIUM, a giant ground sloth
71 MERYCHIPPUS
72 PLIOHIPPUS
73 HIPPARION, a mostly Old-World,
    three-toed horse very like
    Miohippus
74 EQUUS, modern horse
75 DINOTHERIUM
76 SHOVEL TUSKER
77 MASTODON
78 MAMMOTH
79 DIPROTODON, a giant marsupial
80 WOOLLY RHINOCEROS
81 BISON, an extinct bison
82 MACHAIRODUS, an Old-World
    saber-tooth cat
83 SMILODON, a New-World saber-
    tooth cat
84 PROCONSUL
85 AUSTRALOPITHECINES
86 PITHECANTHROPUS
87 NEANDERTHAL MAN

Index

Credits

Aerofilms Ltd.: 15 (middle). American Museum of Natural History: 22 (middle); 23 (right); 35 (below); 40-1 (top) based on material from W. K. Gregory, Evolution Emerging, published by Macmillan and Co.; 46 (below); 50; 54 (below) after Bird; 66 (below) from W. K. Gregory, Evolution Emerging, published by Macmillan and Co.; 79 (two below); 84 (right). British Crown Copyright reserved: 15 (below) Geological Survey photograph, by permission of the Controller, H.M. Stationery Office; 19; 25 from R. L. Sherlock, A Guide to the Geological Column, by permission of the Controller of H.M. Stationery Office; 86. Trustees of the British Museum: 76. Trustees of the British Museum (Natural History): 20 (middle); 22 (top and below); 23 (left); 26; 27; 31 (top and left); 33 (below); 39 (top); 42; 45 (photographs); 55 (below); 56 (below); 58 (top); 59 (below); 62; 78 (middle left); 84 (left); 87; 88 (top). Carnegie Museum: 83 (below). Chicago Natural History Museum: 85. Dr. Edwin H. Colbert: 83 (top). Conzett and Huber, Zurich: 24 (top); 89 (below). Council of the Geological Society of London, and Prof. W. F. Whittard: 31 (right) from plate 4, Q.J.G.S., Vol. 109. Institut Royal des Sciences Naturelles de Belgique: 20 (except middle); 88 (below). London Express: 88 (middle). Los Angeles County Museum: 73. By permission of the Macmillan Company: 69 (below) from William Berryman Scott, A History of Land Mammals in the Western Hemisphere, © 1913. Mansell Collection: 77 (top). McGraw-Hill Book Co. Inc.: 34, from R. C. Moore, Introduction to Historical Geology, 2nd ed. © 1958. Methuen & Co. Ltd.: 15 (top) based on material from Frederick E. Zeuner, Dating the Past, 4th ed. © 1958. Stazione Zoologica Napoli: 32 (below) from Fauna & Flora del Golfo di Napoli. Oxford University Museum: 57 (below); 58 (below). Mrs. F. E. Peabody: 43 Petrolacosaurus, reconstruction by Dr. Frank Peabody. The President and Council of the Royal College of Surgeons of England: 78 (below right) from a pastel sketch by Samuel Lawrence, 1853. Prof. L. Dudley Stamp: 17 (top) from The Earth's Crust. George F. Sternberg and Fort Hays Kansas State College Museum: 80-1 (below) photo by Edward C. Almquist; 89 (top). U.S. Department of the Interior: 24 (below). John Wiley and Sons, Inc.: 14 (top) from J. H. Zumberge, Elements of Geology, © 1958; 82 from Ruben Arthur Stirton, Time Life and Man, © 1959. Zoological Society of London: 41 (top right) Ceratodus forsteri, after Bashford Dean.

Artists' credits

Malcolm Booker: 15 (top and middle); 36 (below); 41 (top right); 57 (top); 69 (below); 75 (top right).
G. Leigh Davies: 32 (below); 39 (below); 40-1 (top); 43; 46 (top); 51; 59 (top); 60; 66 (top); 67.
Peter Sullivan: 19; 26; 34; 42; 58; 68 (below); 80 (top).
Maurice Wilson: Title page; 21; 28-9; 32-3 (top); 35 (top); 36 (top); 37; 38; 41 (below); 44; 47; 48-9; 52-3; 56 (top); 63; 64-5; 68-9 (top and middle); 70-1; 72; 74-5.
Sidney W. Woods: Endpapers; Contents page; 10; 11; 12; 13; 14; 16-7; 24 (below); 25; 54-5 (top); 61; 62; 66 (below); 82; 84 (right); 90-1.

We thank many museums throughout the world without whose help this book could not have been produced, and who continue to guard, yet make accessible the treasures of the past. Our special thanks go to the staff of the British Museum (Natural History), particularly Mr. G. Sawyers, the principal photographer, and to the American Museum of Natural History.

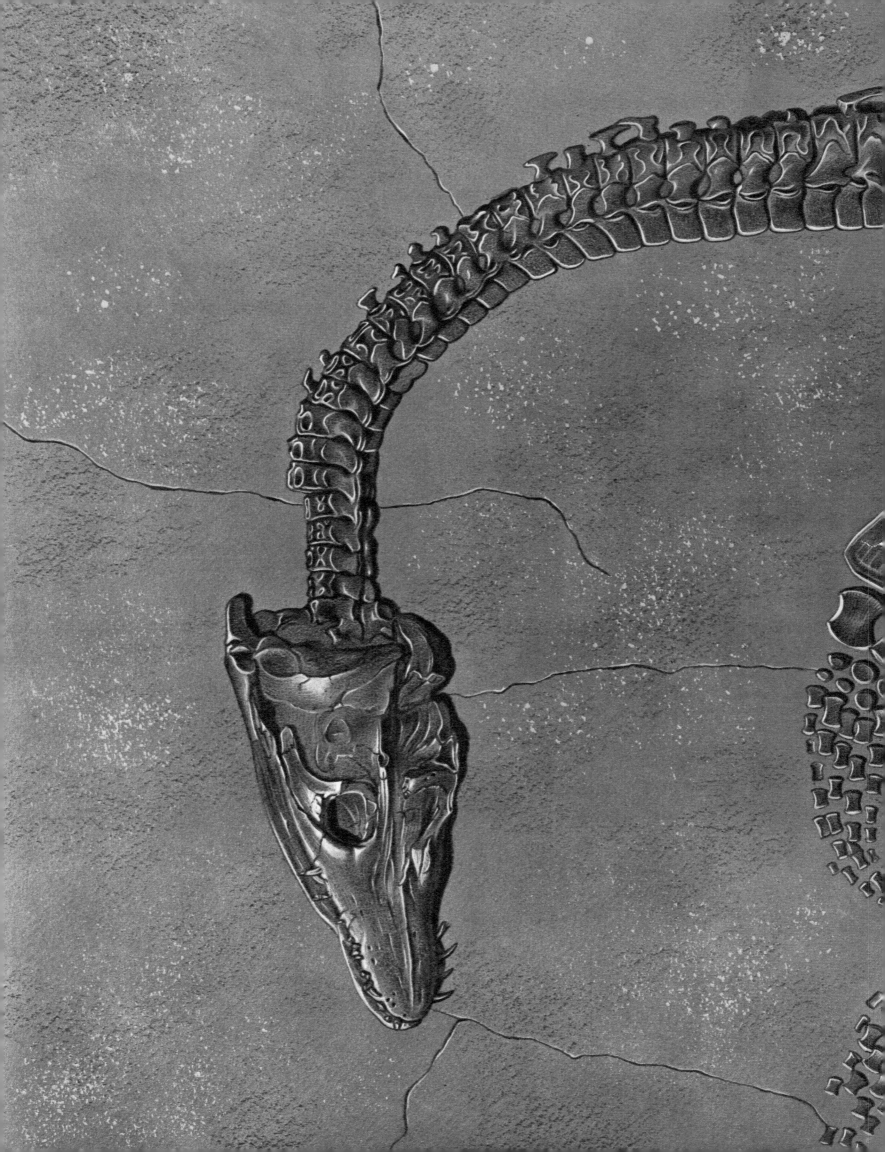